SOUNDS OF LANGUAGE

readers

Enter: Noodles, the ghost.
From now on life will
never be the same!

At some point, you may wish to discuss the title of this book. Historically the Indian powwow has been a gathering of people noted for its vibrant and meaningful sounds. There has been no attempt to liken the *Sounds of a Powwow* to an Indian powwow. However, it does seem appropriate that a book containing so many alive and moving sounds would carry this title.

SOUNDS of a Powwow

TEACHER'S EDITION

GRADE 2

by Bill Martin Jr.
IN COLLABOR-ATION WITH Peggy Brogan

Hello, good teachers. In lieu of talking with you face-to-face, we are relying on man's miraculous invention, print. These annotations, like this reader, are an invitation for all of us to rejoice in the act of language and how it influences man's becoming. The SOUNDS OF LANGUAGE program is designed to enhance a child's use of language as a speaker, a listener, a writer and a reader, and to give you teachers both the opportunities and the skills for bringing

ACKNOWLEDGMENTS

The Author and Holt, Rinehart and Winston, Inc., thank the following authors and publishers, whose help and permissions to reprint materials have made this book possible. All reasonable effort has been made to locate the source of every selection. If any errors in acknowledgments have occurred, they were inadvertent and will be corrected in subsequent editions as they are realized.

Marjorie Barrows, for "Witches' Chant," adapted from "Halloween," by Marjorie Barrows.

Leo Feist, Inc., for "K-K-K-Katy," by Geoffrey O'Hara. Copyright 1918, 1945 by Leo Feist, Inc.

Hill and Range Songs, Inc., and Anne-Rachel Music Corp., for "Three Little Fishes," by Saxie Dowell. Copyright 1939 by Anne-Rachel Music Corp.

Holt, Rinehart and Winston, Inc., for David Was Mad!, by Bill Martin Jr. Copyright © 1967 by Holt, Rinehart and Winston.

Houghton Mifflin, Inc., for "Grizzly Bear," by Mary Austin, from The Children Sing in the Far West, by Mary Austin. Copyright © 1956 by Kenneth M. Chapman and Mary C. Wheelwright.

Betty Jean Martin, for the character, Noodles.

Mary Britton Miller, for "Foal" from MENAGERIE. Used with permission.

Mabel Watts, for "Maytime Magic." Used with permission.

dimensions into the teaching of reading that conventional programs have precluded.

Our essay at the back of this book and the page-by-page annotations are not prescriptive. Nor are they ritual. They offer you up-to-date information about language, about human growth and about classroom organization. They offer a view of the classroom as a launching pad to human greatness, both yours and the children's.

The pupil texts are a collection of stories, poems, songs, essays, pictures and paintings that celebrate the human yen for beauty, excitement, drama, well-being and pleasure. Once you have a rich familiarity with yours and the children's materials in the SOUNDS OF LANGUAGE program, you will have become, we believe, another link in mankind's attempt to stay the chaos of an increasingly hostile world environment.

We believe you will also discover that, without becoming a slave to a teacher's guide, you can fashion day-by-day language encounters that help children claim their human heritage as successful readers.

CONTENTS

Early in the use of this book read the entire Table of Contents aloud to the children, asking them to choose favorites on the basis of titles. You may then use those selections knowing that you do not have to use the selections in any given order. From time to time during the year, come back to the Table of Contents, inviting the children to choose old favorites for their reading time.

This is the first of several "Indian" chants which you will find in this book. Each time the children come to a new chant one half of the group can read the new chant against the one they already know. This means that by the time the children have encountered all six chants the group will actually be divided into 6 parts each reading a different chant. All of the chants contain the lines "shuffle to the left" etc., so that even the six-part reading will have some unison reading. In addition to the fun of this kind of choral reading the children will be developing a word-unlocking skill which is unique to THE SOUNDS OF LAN-GUAGE reading program. This skill involves the use of anticipated rhythm to figure out the actual language. Annotations throughout the book will help develop this skill. First read the chant aloud. Reading across the double spread and keeping the obvious rhythm, then invite the children to read along with you and from that point on you and the children can decide where you want to go with the reading—clapping hands, dividing into boys and girls, etc., etc. You may wish to turn to other chants long before you have reached that part of the book. You can identify the chants by their similarity to the design of this double-page spread.

BEAT BEAT
BEAT BEAT
BEAT BEAT
BEAT BEAT

SHUFFLE to the LEFT

SHUFFLE SHUFFLE   SHUFFLE SHUFFLE
BEAT   BEAT
BEAT   BEAT

INDIAN CHANT

to be read like the beat of a tom-tom

by Bill Martin Jr.   lettering by Eric Carle

BEAT upon the TOM TOM

BEAT upon the DRUM

BEAT upon the TOM TOM

BEAT upon the DRUM

SHUFFLE to the LEFT

SHUFFLE to the LEFT

BEAT upon the TOM TOM

BEAT upon the DRUM

11

Picture reading is the most universally used reading skill. Throughout the SOUNDS OF LANGUAGE program, story telling and discussion pictures with no script are used to invite children to pull in their own meaning and language evoked by the art. There are no right answers. Your role is to appreciate a child's use of a choice word or a well-turned phrase, supporting his ego in its quest for language and language skills.

Here's a Picture for Storytelling

A POEM BY YOUR FRIEND NOODLES
PICTURE BY GEORGE BUCKETT

I'll write you a letter
if you will write me,
but not if I'm stung
by this bumble bee.

13

THE BEAR SONG

To be chanted as a two-part choral reading. Sometimes the second group echoes the first group, but at other times both groups read together, as the color indicates.

The other day The other day
I met a bear I met a bear
out in the woods out in the woods
a way out there. a way out there.

The other day I met a bear

out in the woods a way out there.

out in the woods out in the woods
a way out there. a way out there.

He looked at me. He looked at me.
I looked at him. I looked at him.
He sized me up. He sized me up.
I sized up him. I sized up him.

He looked at me, I looked at him.

He sized me up, I sized up him.

He sized me up. He sized me up.
I sized up him. I sized up him.

Here is another successful reading experience for early second graders. Have the children read in unison. They will be tuning their ears to what their eyes are seeing on the printed page. This helps them build a bridge between the analysis of oral language which they engaged in when they first learned how the language works, and their current analysis of print. It also deposits in their heads the language pattern which they can call on as they read printed language.

He said to me, He said to me,
"Why don't you run? "Why don't you run?
I see you ain't I see you ain't
got any gun." got any gun."
He said to me, "Why don't you run?
I see you ain't got any gun.
I see you ain't I see you ain't
got any gun." got any gun."

I said to him, I said to him,
"That's a good idea, "That's a good idea,
so come on feet, so come on feet,
let's up and fleet. let's up and fleet."
I said to him, "That's a good idea,
so come on feet, let's up and fleet.
so come on feet, so come on feet,
let's up and fleet." let's up and fleet."

AN OLD SONG, AUTHOR UNKNOWN

15

I'm Halloweening!

I'm in-betweening!

I'm magic-making!

I'm ear-drum breaking!

I'm alphabetizing!

I'm skeletonizing!

What Can You Do?

BY NOODLES, DRAWINGS BY RAY BARBER

LOVE SOMEBODY,

LOVE SOMEBODY,

LOVE SOMEBODY,

AND I HOPE SOMEBODY

As the children create their own verses they will be experimenting with the fact that stories and poems have a structure which partially predicts the language that is used. As the children have more experience, our annotations will help develop such knowledge into word-unlocking skills.

18

YES I DO,

YES I DO,

YES I DO,

LOVES ME TOO.

This song can have as many verses as you wish, just by making up new words for YES I DO.

Here are some possibilities:
CAN'T GUESS WHO
LOOKS LIKE YOU
EYES OF BLUE

an old song, lettering by Eric Carle

If the children wish to check this story out of the library, they will discover that it is a book which was illustrated by the author and published by William R. Scott, Inc. What an encouraging experience in individualized reading when the children discover a library book that they can read with ease. The children will learn much about their growing esthetic awareness as they compare the two versions of the story.

a STORY
BY ESPHYR
SLOBODKINA

This story is a childhood favorite, one that they will reread over and over for sheer enjoyment. How they love the antics that go on between the peddler and the monkey, and how they love to act it out reading the lines in parts. As you read aloud invite the children to follow in their books. If they chime right in with you so much the better. At the end of the reading take your cue from the children, they may wish immediately to read it on their own. Incidentally, did the children notice how the title of this story was integrated with the illustration? Their wonderings about designs of this kind stimulate their development of aesthetic taste and awareness.

Caps for Sale

Once there was a peddler See page 60-61 for transforming this sentence.

who went out to sell caps.

He carried the caps

on top of his head.

First he put on his own striped cap,

then four yellow caps,

then four blue caps,

then four red caps.

and on the very top four polkadot caps.

Pixs by
Peter Lippman

Peter Lippman's illustrations for this story should be at some point, studied by the children and discussed irrespective of the text. His techniques, his humor and his obvious joy in the story are deserving of attention.

He walked up and down the streets,
holding himself very straight
so as not to upset his caps.

As he went along he called,
"Caps! Caps for sale! Fifty cents a cap!"

But nobody bought any caps that morning.
Not even a red cap.

Isn't it amazing that the artist has let the tree in this illustration reflect the movement of the peddler? In fact, the tree has his human characteristics!

In time the peddler began to feel
　　very hungry,
but he had no money for lunch.
Not even for a taco.

So he walked and walked
until he came to a great big tree.
"This is a nice place to rest,"
　　thought he.

So he sat down, under the tree
and leaned back
little by little
against the tree-trunk
so as not to upset the caps on his head.

Then he reached up
to make sure that they were straight—
first his own striped cap,
then the four yellow caps,
then the four blue caps,
then the four red caps,
then on the very top the four polkadot caps.

Sentence Transforming:

Then he	went	to sleep.
	wanted	to dream
	started	to buy
	stopped	to eat

Most stories and poems have sentences that are worth manipulating both for the fun and for the linguistic learnings involved. You will want to be sure that the children have enjoyed the literary selections in all of their beauty and wholeness before engaging in such followup activities. Be sure, too, that the children again hear the stories and poems in wholeness after the linguistic manipulations are over.

He slept for a long time.

When he woke up,
he reached up to make sure
that his caps were still on his head.

All he felt was his own striped cap!
The other caps were gone.

By encouraging the children to read this sentence as an exclamation, the use of the exclamation point becomes tangible in their own writing. What their voices can intone in reading their minds can invent for their own writing.

28

He looked to the right of him.
No caps.

He looked to the left of him.
No caps.

He looked in back of him.
No caps.

He looked behind the tree.
No caps.

hopefully   old
quickly   tall

Then — he looked up into the tree.
And what ∧ do you think he saw ∧?

Expanding sentences:

Adding describing words is one good way to expand sentences. As children engage in this linguistic activity, they gain insight into the functions
of various kinds of words in sentences. Gradually
they develop this knowledge into a word-unlocking
skill.

Here is another sentence that invites transforming. Wherever you encounter a sentence that intrigues you or the children you possibly have rich content for sensitizing them to the ways of language.

On every branch there was a monkey.

tree	ghost
corner	man
floor	dog
step	elephant
side	snake

On every monkey there was a cap—
a yellow cap, or a blue cap, or a red cap,
or a polkadot cap!

The peddler looked at the monkeys.

surprised *mischievous playful*

The monkeys looked at the peddler.

Isn't it interesting how the artist has used one tree as the setting for two presentations of story action?

He shook a finger at the monkeys and said,
"You monkeys, you! Give me back my caps!"

The monkeys only shook their fingers back
at him and said, "Tsz, tsz, tsz."

The one monkey above, hanging
head down, gives this illustration
unique dynamics. By blocking the
monkey out with your hand you can
observe this phenomenon.

This made the peddler angry,
so he shook his fist at the monkeys and said,
"You monkeys, you!
Give me back my caps."

But the monkeys only shook their fists
back at him and said,
"Tsz, tsz, tsz."

Now the peddler was quite angry.
He stamped his foot, and said,
"You monkeys, you!
Give me back my caps!"

But the monkeys only stamped their feet
back at him and said,

"Tsz, tsz, tsz." No amount of phonic training could tell you exactly
how to pronounce this sound. Won't it be fun to invite
the children to give their versions?

35

As you encounter innovative arrangements of type in this book, you may be surprised at how confidently your children are willing to attack such pages. We adults have grown accustomed to school books where the same size and style of type move relentlessly from left to right, page after page, and it is easy to forget that today's children are encountering imaginative and flamboyant uses of type on T.V., in magazine advertising and even on their cereal boxes. How appropriate that school books too can call upon imaginative and intriguing page design in an effort to bring new dimensions to the children's linguistic learnings and to convince today's young readers that there is much that is alive and gripping between the covers of a book.

At last the peddler became so angry that he pulled off his cap and threw it on the ground.

Then, each monkey pulled off his cap…

and all the yellow caps…

and all the blue caps…

and all the red caps…

and all the polkadot caps…

came flying down out of the tree.

So the peddler picked up his caps
and put them back on his head—

An excursion to the dictionary will help the children discover the three spellings for the word "peddler." Perhaps you can think of other words with more than one spelling to add to the list which you can begin today.

first his own striped cap,

then the four yellow caps,

then the four blue caps,

then the four red caps,

then the four polkadot caps on the very top.

And slowly, he walked away calling,

Isn't it interesting that in English sentences, the number precedes other describing words. We simply wouldn't say *yellow four caps*. This kind of knowledge about word-order is developed into a word-unlocking skill in SOUNDS OF LANGUAGE.

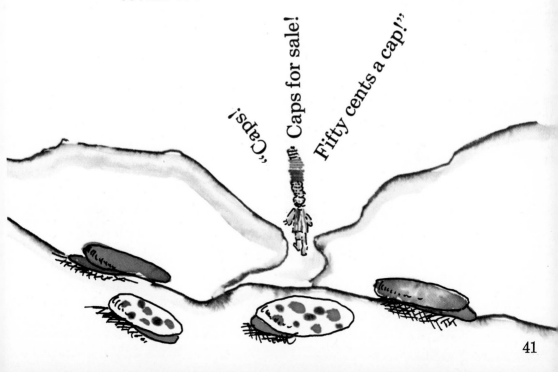

"Caps! Caps for sale! Fifty cents a cap!"

Here is the second of the "Indian" chants which can be read against the others in the book. This particular chant could be enigmatic because the rhythm does not immediately reveal itself. Rather than for you to tell the children how to read it, how much better to let them experiment by reading it against the first chant on page 10. The key to the rhythm is in reading the words, "jingle, jangle" while the other group is reading the word "beat".

JINGLE JANGLE *JINGLE JANGLE*

JINGLE JANGLE JINGLE JANGLE

JINGLE JANGLE JINGLE JANGLE

JINGLE JANGLE *JINGLE JANGLE*

SHUFFLE to the LEFT

SHUFFLE SHUFFLE   SHUFFLE SHUFFLE

JINGLE JANGLE *JINGLE JANGLE*

JINGLE JANGLE JINGLE JANGLE

JINGLE JANGLE CHANT

to be read like the beat of a tom-tom
by Bill Martin Jr.   lettering by Eric Carle

JINGLE   at the   WRIST BELL

JINGLE   at the   KNEE BELL

JINGLE   at the   WRIST BELL

JINGLE   at the   KNEE BELL

SHUFFLE   to the   LEFT

SHUFFLE   to the   LEFT

JINGLE   at the   WRIST BELL

JINGLE   at the   KNEE BELL

43

If the children wish to turn from page to page
enjoying the artist's childlike drawings before
you even begin the reading, encourage them

Five Little Chickens

to do so. This self-initiated exploration of a
story during which a child tunes himself up
for the reading is a reading skill in itself.

Said the first little chicken
With a queer little squirm,

See p. 190-191 to find this
sentence transformed.
Once the children see the
fun involved, invite them
to choose other sentences
for transforming.

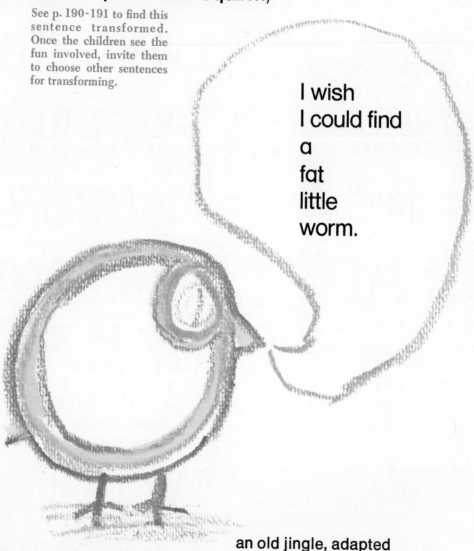

I wish
I could find
a
fat
little
worm.

an old jingle, adapted

Said the second little chicken
With a queer little shrug,

I wish
I could find
a
fat
little
bug.

with crayon drawings by, André François

45

Most materials in this book and throughout the SOUNDS OF LANGUAGE program tend to be rhythmical and rhyming. There is a reason. Highly structured stories and poems more readily impress themselves upon the ear and are, therefore, more readily accessible to the tongue than straight prose. Since the ear and the tongue have a definite influence on what the eye is seeing, the SOUNDS OF LANGUAGE program deals first with the ear and the tongue and subsequently with the eye in releasing children to the printed page. You, therefore, may want to read and reread this story many, many times, inviting the children to chime in whenever they have developed a familiarity with the story line. Afterwards you will see the children taking the book from the reading table and addressing themselves to word recognition as they are mouthing the story. You do not need a standardized test to know when this phenomenon is occurring and the children are actually recognizing words.

Said the third little chicken
With a queer little tug,

I wish
I could find
a
fat
little
slug.

Isn't it interesting that part of this sentence could be rearranged ("the fourth little chicken said") while others cannot ("the little fourth chicken").

A basic characteristic of the English language is the fact that certain words come in front of other words. The children's ears have already picked up this fact, and now you can help them use it to unlock printed language.

Said the fourth little chicken
With a queer little nod,

I wish
I could find
a
butterbean
pod.

This story is hung together with ordinal numbers, a rhyme scheme, and a repeated introductory phrase. Once the children have discovered this, they may wish to borrow the author's literary structure and innovate with ideas of their own. How nice if you can add to your reading table several stories of the children that are built on this structure. Children who have this kind of experience will find themselves using their understanding of an author's literary structure to read words that they didn't know they knew. This skill is developed in the SOUNDS OF LANGUAGE reading program.

Said the fifth little chicken
With a queer little sigh,

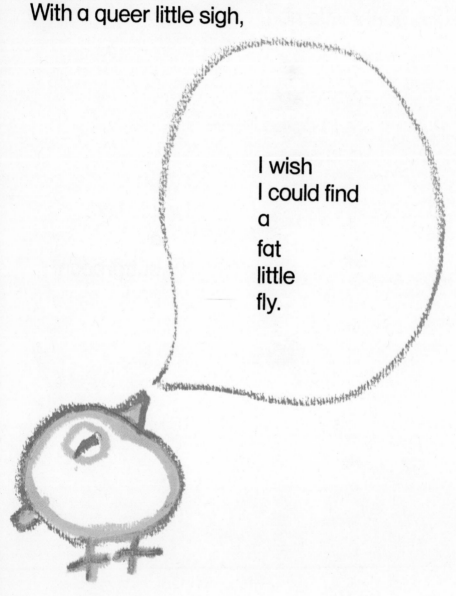

I wish
I could find
a
fat
little
fly.

Said the old mother hen
From the green garden-patch,

If you want
any breakfast,
just come here
and scratch!

I'm too little,
Mother.

I'm too busy,
Mother.

What an interesting bulletin board
if every child drew a picture of himself as a chicken with a comic "bal-
loon" encasing his reason for not
wanting "to scratch."

I can't scratch,
Mother.

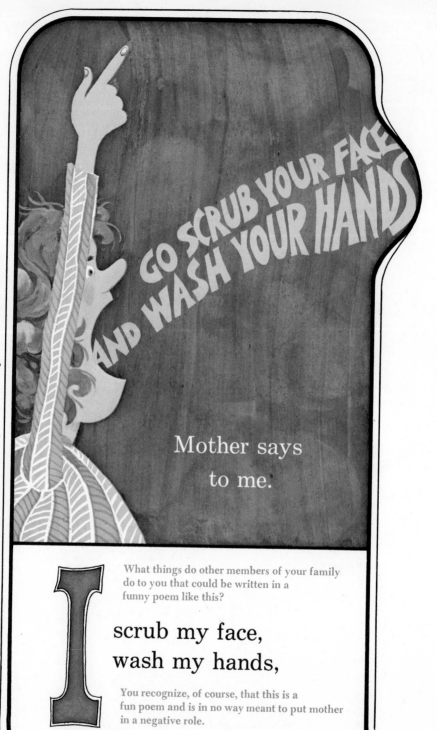

GO SCRUB YOUR FACE
AND WASH YOUR HANDS

Mother says
to me.

by Lucia and James L. Hymes, Jr. with pictures by Ted Schroeder

What things do other members of your family do to you that could be written in a funny poem like this?

I scrub my face,
wash my hands,

You recognize, of course, that this is a fun poem and is in no way meant to put mother in a negative role.

And come to let her see.

52

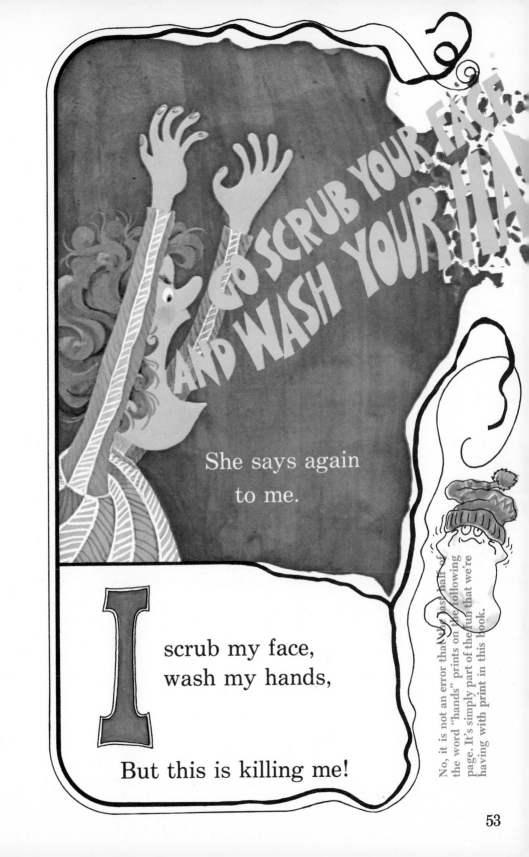

"GO SCRUB YOUR FACE AND WASH YOUR HA!"

She says again
to me.

I scrub my face,
wash my hands,

But this is killing me!

No, it is not an error that the last half of the word "hands" prints on the following page. It's simply part of the fun that we're having with print in this book.

An Afternoon Snack

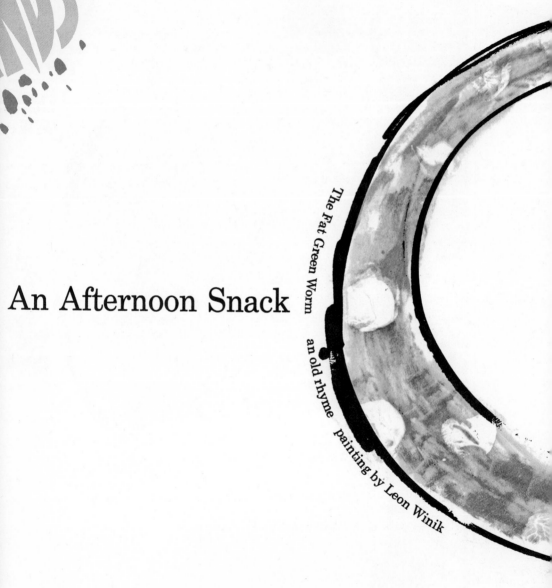

The Fat Green Worm

an old rhyme

painting by Leon Winik

Children love jokes! What fun to discover that a play on words can create this piece of humor. Invite the children to write their own creations for playing with words. Their ideas may amaze you.

I WON IT,
YOU TWO IT,
I THREE IT,
YOU FOUR IT,
I FIVE IT,
YOU SIX IT,
I SEVEN IT,

YOU EIGHT IT!

How many words can the children find that pattern like "eight" and "ate," words that are spelled differently but sound alike? Why not start a list on the bulletin board today and keep adding to it?

Here's a Picture To Dream About by E. Garcia Yata

The poet created his first images around phrasing, "In the night." In the second stanza he transformed the first by changing "night" to "day." No doubt your children could do a similar piece of writing by starting a poem with "In the summer" and then transforming the second stanza to read "In the winter." Awarenesses of this kind give children greater power in their use of language, including reading, writing and speaking.

In the night,
    opossum;
in the night,
the owl;
in the night
the bat—
and coyote
on the prowl.

In the day
    the butterfly;
in the day
the bee;
in the day
the hummingbird—
and a deer
beneath a tree.

a poem by James Steel Smith

Poem and Picture

a song by Geoffrey O'Hara, picture by George Buckett

K-K-K-Katy,
beautiful Katy,
you're the only
g-g-g-girl
that I adore.
When the m-moon
shines
over the cow shed,
I'll be waiting at
the kitty-k-kitchen
door.

What a nice time to review beginning consonants.

These pages give children the visual picture of sentence transforming. If they have already been transforming sentences on their own, they may be able to immediately create new sentences from the possibilities offered. However, if they have not been transforming sentences before now, you will want to read with them the vocabulary choices so they will have full freedom to enjoy creating sentences of their choice.

Once   was   a   peddler

⎡ One day ⎤ there ⎡ were ⎤ ⎡ two ⎤   ⎡ dog (s)
⎣ Long ago ⎦   ⎣   ⎦ ⎣ many ⎦ │ monkey (s)
                                        │ ghost (s)
                                        │ pieman
                                        ⎣ piemen

How many different sentences can you make using this sentence for a pattern?

who
went	out	to sell	caps.
flew	in	to eat	cookies
jumped	by	to scare	people
ran	through	to cook	spinach
sneaked	about	to make	apples
crawled		to buy	dirt
			noise
			skeletons

PUZZLE

61

Complete familiarity with the first three verses of this old poem should become part of the children's chanting experiences before you attempt to take them into the structured experiences outlined from the fourth verse through the tenth. They cannot easily create the last six verses, unless they first possess the basic structure to use as the tool. Moreover, familiarity with this basic structure is the essential tool for their reading of the "baby talk" in "Three Little Fishes" beginning on page 182.

Over in the Meadow in the sand in the sun
Lived an old mother turtle and her little turtle one.
"Dig," said the mother.
"I dig," said the one.
So they dug all day in the sand in the sun.

an old rhyme
pictures by Eric Carle

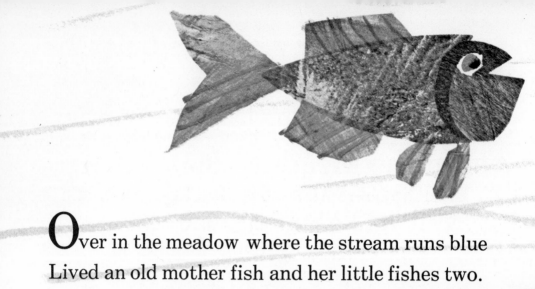

Over in the meadow where the stream runs blue
Lived an old mother fish and her little fishes two.
"Swim," said the mother.
"We swim," said the two.
So they swam all day where the
stream runs blue.

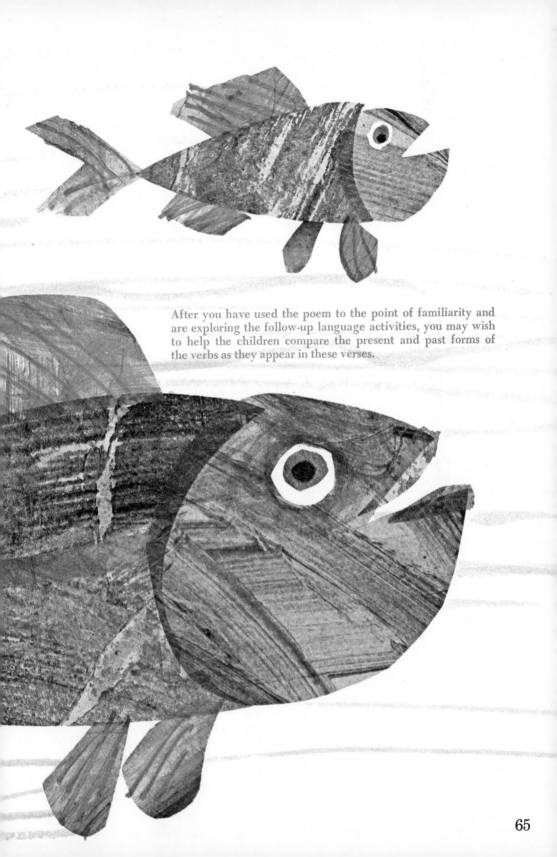

After you have used the poem to the point of familiarity and are exploring the follow-up language activities, you may wish to help the children compare the present and past forms of the verbs as they appear in these verses.

Over in the meadow
    in a hole in a tree
Lived an old mother owl
    and her little owls three.
        "Tu-whoo,"
    said the mother.
        "We tu-whoo,"
    said the three.
So they tu-whoo'd all night
    in a hole in a tree.

NOW THAT YOU HAVE READ

the first three verses of this old rhyme,
you can use the clues that follow
to help you figure out
how the rest of the rhyme goes:

The first four words of each verse
are exactly the same.

The next few words tell where
the creatures live.

The next few words tell who the mother is and how many babies she has.

 The mother tells the babies to do something and they obey.

 The verse ends by repeating what the babies did and where they were.

NOW, FIGURE OUT THE FOURTH VERSE.

GNAW

Over __ __ __
__ __ old barn door
Lived __ __ __ __
__ __ __ __ __.
     "Gnaw," __ __ __.
     "__ __," __ __ __.
So __ __ __ __
__ __ __ __ __.

As the children fill in the missing words they are experiencing the fact that the knowledge of a story or poem's literary structure can help a person decode print.

In each succeeding verse the children are given fewer and fewer clues, causing them to rely more heavily on their accumulated knowledge of the poem's structure. You can help them enjoy their linguistic success by pointing out, after they have completed the tenth verse, that with only two clues they patterned thirty eight words into language.

5 Over __ __ __

in a sunny beehive

Lived __ __ __ __

__ __ __ __ __.

"Buzz," __ __ __.

"__ __," __ __ __.

So __ __ __ __

__ __ __ __.

6 — — — —
in a nest made of sticks
Lived — — — —
— — — — —.
     "Caw," — — —.
     "— —," — — —.
So — — — — —
— — — — — —.

7
— — — —
where the grass grows even
Lived — — — —
— — — — —.
     "—," — — —.
     "— —," — — —.
So — — — —
— — — — —.

NOW FOR THE EIGHTH VERSE

__ __ __ __
by the old mossy gate
__ __ __ __ __
__ __ __ __ __.
        "__," __ __ __.
        "__ __," __ __ __.
So __ __ __ __
        __ __ __ __.

9 __ __ __ __
by the old Scotch pine
__ __ __ __
__ __ __ __.
        "__," __ __ __.
        "__ __," __ __ __.
__ __ __ __
        __ __ __ __.

10

__ __ __ __

__ __ cozy wee den

__ __ __ __ __

__ __ __ __ __ .

"__," __ __ __ .

"__ __," __ __ .

__ __ __ __ __

__ __ __ __ __ .

73

The children may enjoy looking for this title, "Four Fur Feet," in the library. It is a delightfully illustrated book published by William R. Scott Inc.

This language experience has inordinate charm. It is the kind of experience that children love to repeat over and over and over again, as they experience the joy of each word falling into its appropriate place. We have used the poem as a vehicle for language intrigue. Let the children figure out, without your telling, which sentence follows which. For example, how long will it take them to discover that page 79 is read from the bottom to the top? Or that the poem begins on the right hand page and then moves to the left, then back to the right? The verses on page 76 and 77 read counterclockwise. What fun the children will have turning their books in continuous discovery. Do not be worried about an experience of this kind inculcating faulty reading habits. The utter delight with which children solve the linguistic rhythms, and the welcome relief that the print offers some children by breaking cultural tradition, are reasons enough for inclusion. As Sir John Dalton observed, "Happiness first. All else follows."

THE WORLD on his four fur feet,
his four fur feet,
his four fur feet.

Four Fur Feet

OH, HE WALKED AROUND

And he walked
around the world
on his four fur feet
and never made
a sound—O.

Have the children noticed
in how many ways the de-
signer used type to suggest
walking around the world? Perhaps the children would like to
experiment with this notion in
their own writing. They may be
mightily relieved to discover that in
their own stories they need not relentlessly move from left to right, and
that they can actually design their words to
take the place of illustrations.

a poem by Margaret Wise Brown
designed by Bill Martin Jr.

OH, he walked along the river
on his four fur feet,
his four fur feet,
his four fur feet.
He walked along the river
on his four fur feet
and heard the boats go toot—O.

THEN he walked by the railroad
on his four fur feet,
his four fur feet,
his four fur feet.
He walked by the railroad
on his four fur feet
and heard the trains go whoo—O.

THEN he waded down a stream
on his four fur feet,
his four fur feet,
his four fur feet.
He waded down a stream
on his four fur feet.
and the water was all wet—O.

THEN he walked into the country
on his four fur feet,
his four fur feet,
his four fur feet.
He walked into the country
on his four fur feet
and heard the cows go moo—O.

SO he folded up
his four fur feet,
his four fur feet,
his four fur feet.
So he folded up
his four fur feet
and lay down in
the grass—O.
And the sun
shone down
on his four fur feet,
his four fur feet,
his four fur feet.
And the sun shone down
on his four fur feet
and made them feel all warm—O.

and never made a sound—O.
on his four fur feet
    And he walked around the world
      his four fur feet.
        his four fur feet,
          on his four fur feet,
          around the world
          walked
          he
          And
          was round—O.
          that all the world
        he dreamed a dream
      And as he slept
    dreamed a dream.
dreamed a dream,
he dreamed a dream,
AND as he slept

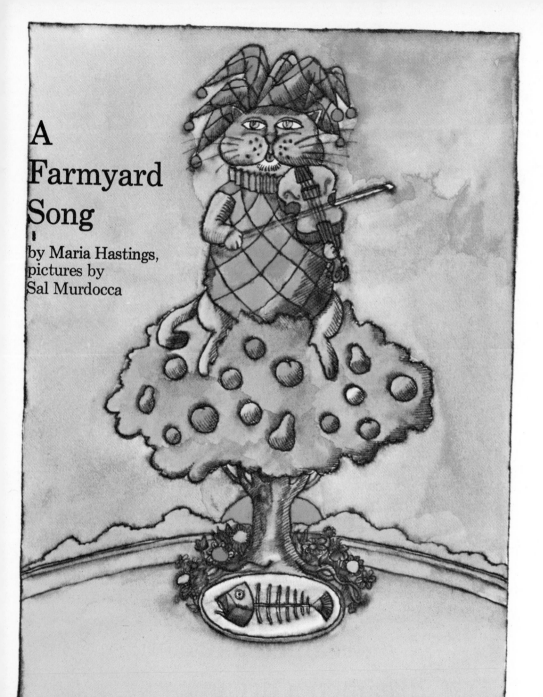

A Farmyard Song

by Maria Hastings,
pictures by
Sal Murdocca

I had a cat and the cat pleased me,
I fed my cat by yonder tree;
    Cat goes fiddle-i-fee.

Once the children discover that this is a cumulative poem, each new verse building on the preceding one—they will have the structural clues needed to interpret

I had a hen and the hen pleased me,
I fed my hen by yonder tree;
  Hen goes chimmy-chuck, chimmy-chuck,
  Cat goes fiddle-i-fee.

the picture on pages 88 and 89, and the brief script given in the final verse.

I had a duck and the duck pleased me,
I fed my duck by yonder tree;
Duck goes quack, quack,
Hen goes chimmy-chuck, chimmy-chuck,
Cat goes fiddle-i-fee.

Here is a jingle that can be read in parts with each child or group of children taking the part of the farmer or an animal.

I had a sheep and the sheep pleased me,
I fed my sheep by yonder tree,
  Sheep goes baa, baa,
  Duck goes quack, quack,
  Hen goes chimmy-chuck, chimmy-chuck,
  Cat goes fiddle-i-fee.

I had a pig and the pig pleased me,
I fed my pig by yonder tree;
  Pig goes griffy, gruffy,
  Sheep goes baa, baa,
  Duck goes quack, quack,
  Hen goes chimmy-chuck, chimmy-chuck,
  Cat goes fiddle-i-fee.

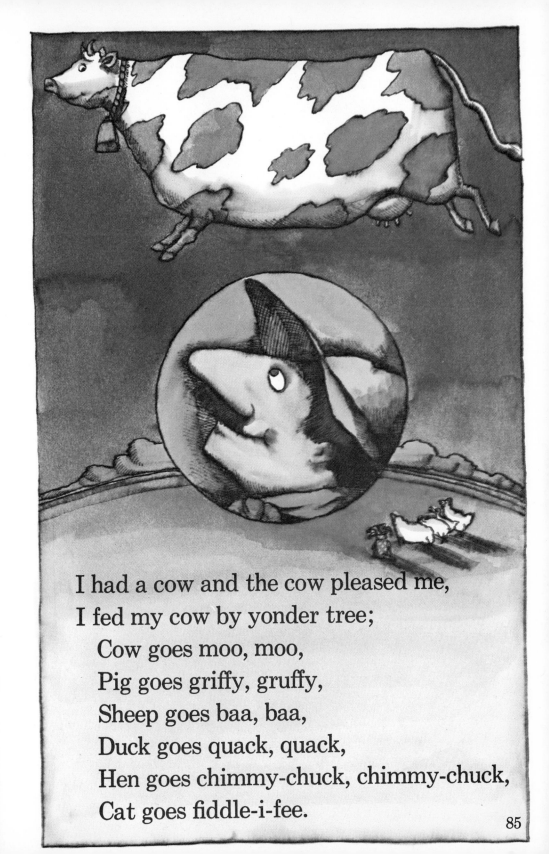

I had a cow and the cow pleased me,
I fed my cow by yonder tree;
   Cow goes moo, moo,
   Pig goes griffy, gruffy,
   Sheep goes baa, baa,
   Duck goes quack, quack,
   Hen goes chimmy-chuck, chimmy-chuck,
   Cat goes fiddle-i-fee.

I had a dog and the dog pleased me,
I fed my dog by yonder tree;
　Dog goes bow-wow,
　Cow goes moo, moo,
　Pig goes griffy, gruffy,
　Sheep goes baa, baa,
　Duck goes quack, quack,
　Hen goes chimmy-chuck, chimmy-chuck,
　Cat goes fiddle-i-fee.

A Story

Prepare for an adventure in fantasy. Prepare also for the real delight the children will feel when they recognize that here is an author who uses the same intriguing kind of sequence that they so often like to create in their own writing. How fortunate that no one told this author he couldn't use abbreviations, great flights in the lack of continuity and wonderful incongruities! The success of this story is its fidelity to the ways of childhood. In your first reading of it to the children and subsequently their reading of it for their own delight, the linguistic continuity should be maintained. If on occasions you wish to go through simply to discuss and react to the pictures, let that be an experience in itself. To try to integrate story continuity with open discussion tends to dilute the value of both.

The little spaceman came down & landed in her backyard.

This story abounds in sentences to transform.

You may be amazed at the ease with which the children will read this lovely script even if they have never had cursive writing.

Have you noticed the beautiful hand lettering used for this story? As you look at a double-page spread, do you have the feeling that the pictures and the words and the space all create the message? This was the intention of the author-artist. The value of this story cannot be measured by the number of words on a page. Its message is in the utter delight it offers a child, helping him stay the chaos of the day. Throughout the SOUNDS OF LANGUAGE program we have introduced book experiences of this kind. We invite you to respond with joy knowing that "what the heart feels today, the head will know tomorrow."

She took him by the ear &
threw him in
a pit

and grew him like a vegetable.

Up he came

Rearranging sentences:
When children recognize that many sentences can be rearranged because they have movable parts, the children become more skilled as sentence readers and writers. On pages 97 and 99 is a sentence that can be rearranged in a variety of ways.

He came up by the hundreds.
By the hundreds he came up.

by the hundreds.

At her he sprang

and
took her away in his spaceship

and stuck her in the ground
on his own planet.

She didn't know
what to do;
so she grew;

How nice to have 12 pages and 6 illustrations to help the children appreciate the structure of a single sentence.

*and when
there was enough of her,*

she jumped
on the spaceship
&

sailed home

and put herself
    back together

again.

Sound your *clucks*, everybody!
We're going to do
a choral reading of this old rhyme.
The teacher can read the story lines,
you read
the *clucks* and *quacks*
and *peeps*.
Only don't do them too loud
because I'm sitting on my eggs.

The hen to herself said one beautiful day,

Cluck, Cluck.

The day is so fine, I'll step over the way,
Cluck, cluck.
And call on my neighbor and friend Madam Duck,
Who lives on the opposite side of the brook,
"Cluck, cluck, cluck, cluck, cluck, cluck."

So, smoothing her feathers, she called to her chicks,

Cluck, Cluck.

And bade them be sure to keep in her tracks,
Cluck, cluck.
For having no one to attend them at home,
She had to take them when abroad she did roam,
"Cluck, cluck, cluck, cluck, cluck, cluck."

An Old Story

ART BY RAY BARBER

"Good day, Madam Hen," said the duck with a bow,

Quack, Quack.

"I hope you are well and your dear chickens too,"

Quack, Quack.

"And now let them go with my ducklings and play,
While we have a chat on the news of the day,

Quack, Quack,

Quack, Quack,

Quack, Quack."

So off went the chickens and ducklings to play,

Peep, Peep.

And straight to the brook the young ducks led the way,

Quack, Quack.

Right into the water they went without fear,
And called to the chickens to follow them there,
"Peep, peep, peep, peep, peep, peep."

The ducklings so easily swam all about,

Quack, Quack,

The chickens said, "Surely 'tis easy to float,

Peep, Peep."

So in they all went, but alas, they soon found
That chicks are not ducks
for the brood nearly drowned.
"Peep, peep, peep, peep, peep, peep."

I am an old, **Old Mouse**
Who lives in an old, old house.
I have a long tail and pointed ears;
I've been living here for seventy-two years;
I have sixteen sisters and nineteen brothers;
Also living with us are twenty-seven others.
We are a very jolly bunch
Especially when we eat our lunch.
I am the oldest of us mice.
Come to think of it, it's kind of nice.

BY A THIRD GRADE BOY,
PICTURE BY KIYOAKI KOMODA

117

Spring is coming, spring is coming,
All around is fair,

Suddenly it's summer,
Joy is everywhere.

By William Blake

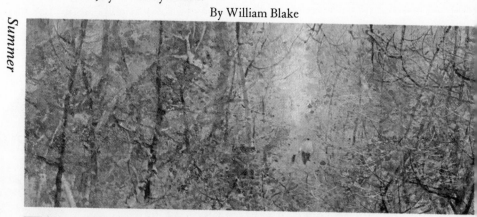

The Four Seasons by Chen Chi

Chen Chi is a foremost painter of the seasons, as even children will observe in these lovely pictures. We have included his work and the work of other fine artists in these books believing that children should have consistent exposure to the aesthetic realms of life, as well as to the factual. You can use picture reading experiences for many purposes: painting, meditating discussing, creative writing, or for evaluating styles of art. This double-page spread and the one that follows have used white space as part of the pictorial design. Are the children becoming aware of the relationship of a picture to the space in which it rides?

Yellow the bracken,
Golden the sheaves,
Rosy the apples,
Crimson the leaves;

Mist on the hillside,
Clouds grey and white.
Autumn, good morning!
Summer, good night.

By Florence Hoatson

Winter

The North wind doth blow,
And we shall have snow,
And what will the children do then, poor things?

They'll slide on the hill,
Until they are ill,
And get to miss school all week, poor things!

A LAMENT BY YOUR FRIEND NOODLES

Foal

Come trotting up
Beside your mother,
Little skinny.

Lay your neck across
Her back, and whinny,
Little foal.

You think you're a horse
Because you can trot—
But you're not.

Your eyes
    are so wild,
And each leg
    is as tall
As a pole;
And you're only
    a skittish
Child, after all,
Little foal.

BY MARY BRITTON MILLER,
PICTURE BY ED YOUNG

This poem by Mary Britton Miller is first of all a memorable literary experience, and it should be enjoyed as such. Your reading it aloud several times as a listening experience prepares children for dealing with it as poetry when they first meet it in printed form. Nothing can be worse for children than having to struggle with unknown words when they are developing sensitivities to poetic patterns! Word recognition skills follow logically and surely in the wake of a child's intimate familiarity with the sentence sounds he is to read. Our first job in reading instruction, therefore, is to read aloud to children and then to help them see similarities between what they are hearing and what they are seeing.

Here's another "Indian" chant that works against the others you have found in the book. It might be appropriate at this time in the children's identification with the chant to point out that sometimes two words work against a single beat (*i.e.*, "sliding down") and other times four syllables (*i.e.*, "wearing out their").

The intuitive response of a reader of poetry to feel the underlying rhythm of a poem and to pit certain sequences of syllables against a single beat within the rhythm is essential. Obvious chants such as this one are beginning stages in helping children mature in their understanding of the rhythms of language.

ONE LITTLE, TWO LITTLE,

FLYING OVER HAYSTACKS,

SLIDING DOWN MOONBEAMS,

HI HO

SHUFFLE to the LEFT,

SHUFFLE SHUFFLE   SHUFFLE SHUFFLE

ONE LITTLE, TWO LITTLE,

HI HO

WITCHES' CHANT

to be read like the beat of a tom-tom

an adaptation by Bill Martin Jr. from "Three Little Witches" by Marjorie Barrows

lettering by Eric Carle

THREE LITTLE WITCHES,
FLYING OVER DITCHES
WEARING OUT THEIR BRITCHES.
HALLOWEEN'S HERE !

SHUFFLE to the LEFT,
SHUFFLE to the LEFT,
THREE LITTLE WITCHES,
HALLOWEEN'S HERE !

Here's a Picture to Talk About

PAINTING BY RONALD THOMASON

Ronald

The Fireghost

**A PICTURE STORY BY MONIKA BEISNER,
ADAPTED BY BILL MARTIN JR.**

Here is a charming prose poem which invites children
to take part in the entire linguistic cycle—listening,
speaking, reading, writing.

As you read aloud the children will soon chime right
in. At the end of the children's reading, you can use
this poem in many different ways on different occasions. One day you may wish to use it for triggering
creative writing. The children may enjoy knowing
that the scientists say there are four basic elements:
fire, water, air, and earth. Some children may then
want to try their hand at writing a prose poem about
one of the other three elements. What fun they will
have when they discover in third grade that the same
author has written the same kind of a selection about
water. Other children may simply wish to borrow the
clear-cut structure for writing about any subject that
intrigues them. On another occasion you may wish to
discuss the art. Give the children opportunities to experiment with their own drawings and paintings of
fire.

*Fireghost Fari
suddenly
rises,
looking for me.*

The artist's concept of fire may trigger off discussions of the fire of volcanos, and of stars, such as our sun. As children accumulate information about these or any other subjects, their understandings tend to be amalgamated and generalized through pictorial decorations added to their written pages. The artistic expression of a concept should be just as welcome in color and line as it is in word language.

Fireghost Fari
flamingly
belches,
calling for me.

The cumulative nature of the sequence of drawings in this story is not unlike the cumulative nature of the jingle "A Farmyard Song" beginning on Page 80. Considerations of this kind help children become more aware of certain literary and pictorial styles.

Fireghost Fari
angrily
lurches,
hunting for me.

Have you noticed how open-ended the meanings are in this story? The children will probably get into lively spontaneous discussions as they try to decide who *me* is and what actually happens at the end. Does Fari know his search is hopeless? Is the search just going to continue forever? Luckily, there are no right answers to such questions. One child's interpretation is as valid as another's. This is how it should be in reading a story or poem. There are two people in the transaction—the author and the person doing the reading. For a discussion of ways for handling this open-ended view of comprehension, see TE page 107.

Fireghost Fari wildly searches, cursing me.

The children may be interested to know that the word *cursing* does not refer to the use of swear words. It means to cast a hex.

These two poems, written by young children, will do much to encourage the writing of poetry by children in your class. The poem at the right is designed in the shape of its message. This type of design in poetry is called concrete poetry—in other words, the poem looks like what it is about. A child writing about a fish could be encouraged to position the lines in the shape of a fish. The concrete poem technique often releases a child to the use of language that otherwise might not have found expression. The children will be pleased to know that a poet has great freedom in deciding how to punctuate his poem. No one, not even an editor, would change the poet's punctuation. Notice the punctuation in the poem on this page. You also might invite the children to find other words beginning with consonant blends that express the sounds they represent (block-block, chop-chop, click-click).

Tina Anthony
AGE 7
ENGLAND

Poems from *Miracles* by Richard Lewis

A little egg
in a nest of hay.
cheep-cheep.
crack-crack.
a little chick
pecked his shell away
cheep-cheep.
crack-crack.

I LOVE YOU, BIG WORLD. I wish I could call you And tell you a secret: That I love you, World... I love you, World...

by *Paul Wollner*
AGE 7
UNITED STATES

A Picture for Storytelling by George Buckett

Here is a plot situation—Noodles the little ghost baked inside a gingerbread boy—that should trigger all kinds of creative storytelling and story writing in your class. Children need a wellspring of emotion and/or story thrust to ease their experiences in creative expression.

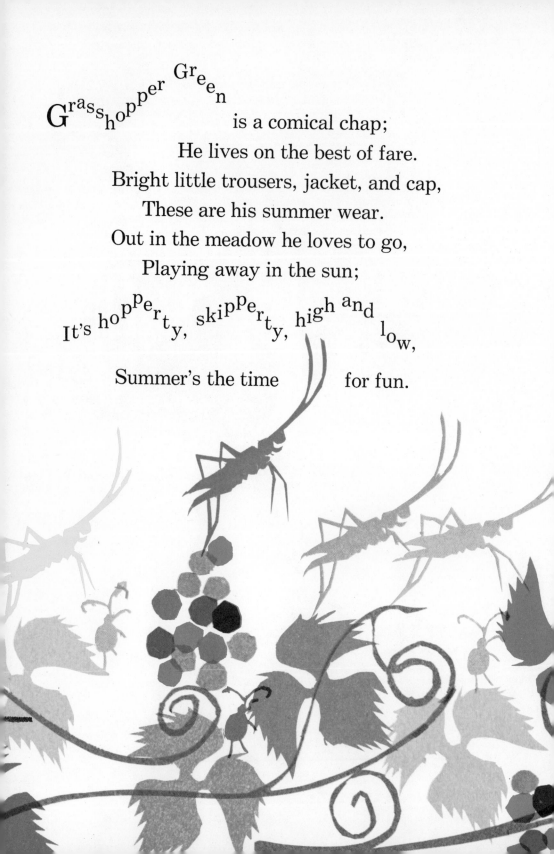

Grasshopper Green
is a comical chap;
He lives on the best of fare.
Bright little trousers, jacket, and cap,
These are his summer wear.
Out in the meadow he loves to go,
Playing away in the sun;
It's hopperty, skipperty, high and low,
Summer's the time for fun.

How intriguing when special words can look like the meaning they represent! Some highly visual children actually decode print this way. Rather than seeing phonic elements or spelling patterns in words, they see pictures. It is harmful to require these children to sound-out words until they have had ample time to decode print in the way that works best for them. Once they feel successful, they won't mind adding phonics to their accumulation of decoding skills.

Grasshopper Green has a quaint little house;

It's under the hedge so gay.

Grandmother Spider, as still as a mouse,

Watches him over the way.

Gladly he's calling the children, I know,

Out in the beautiful sun;

It's hopperty, skipperty, high and low,

Summer's the time for fun.

OLD RHYME, COLLAGE BY CAROL KOFOD BUTTERFIELD

Once upon a time

there was a turtle.

He wasn't a big turtle,

nor a middle-sized turtle,

but just a little turtle.

And he lived in a small garden

that had a little pool in it.

Here is a worthwhile sentence for expanding. How many describing words can the children place in front of the words *house* and *kitten?*

In the house next door
there was a kitten.
Not a big kitten,
nor a middle-sized kitten,
but just a little kitten.
And he was a very curious little kitten
at that.

story *The Curious Little Kitten* by Bernadine Cook, pictures by Remy Charlip

Every day the little turtle

would walk around in the garden.

Now, turtles cannot go very fast

because their legs are so short.

So they go slowly.

So, the little turtle walked around the garden

slowly, very slowly.

He would stop,

lift up his head,

and then he would go again.

One day

he was walking around like this,

You will observe on this page that the double page is divided into two portions, an upper half and a lower half, both of which extend from one margin to another. The type in the top portion of the spread is, therefore, read in its entirety before moving to the lower portion of the page. Later on in this story when the page is divided into three equal sections the children may need to be reminded that the sequence of reading is not up and down from top to bottom, but across the section.

when the curious little kitten
ventured into the garden.

Now, the little kitten
had never seen a turtle before,
because he was just a little kitten
and he hadn't been around very much.
He was surprised.
He stopped and looked at the turtle.

The little turtle stopped.
And the little kitten stopped.

The little turtle looked at the kitten.
    And the little kitten looked at the turtle.

Then...

the little kitten slapped at the turtle
with one little paw.
The little kitten's eyes nearly popped right out!
Because—do you know what happened?

The little turtle's head disappeared!
Just like that!
He pulled it right inside
his little turtle shell!

Well!

The little kitten took a step backwards.
And then he sat down.

Pretty soon the little kitten got up,
and walked around the little turtle,
very slowly and very carefully.
He looked at this funny creature
that could make his head disappear.
Maybe, he thought,
if I slap at him again,
his head will come out.

So he slapped him again.
The little kitten's eyes
nearly popped out a second time!
Because—do you know what happened?

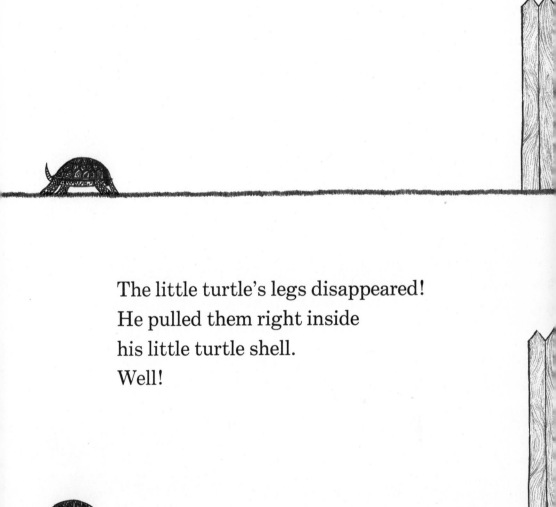

The little turtle's legs disappeared!
He pulled them right inside
his little turtle shell.
Well!

The little kitten
didn't know quite what to think.
So he just stood right there,
looking at the little turtle.

This story is also a distinguished children's book published by William R. Scott. The children might enjoy finding it in the library. The enjoyment of a story tends to be enhanced when children find it in various formats and in various places.

And the little turtle sat right there
inside his little turtle shell.

The little kitten
took a step backwards.

And the little kitten
took another step
backwards.

Pretty soon the little turtle
began to let his legs down out of his shell again,
very slowly.

Then the little turtle poked his little nose
out of his little turtle shell.

Then the little turtle poked his whole head
out of his little turtle shell.

And the little kitten took another step backwards.

The little kitten took another step backwards
...and another.

The little turtle took a step toward the kitten.

The little turtle took another step toward the kitten
…and another.

The little turtle took one more step.
And, oh, my!

The little kitten fell

Splash!

backwards
right into the pool of water.

Now, kittens don't like water
except to drink.
So the little kitten jumped out of the water
and ran past the turtle
as fast as he could run…

But the little turtle kept right on going,
and slid down into the water,
because turtles just love water.

…right back home
where he belonged.

This is a fine story for acting out as a straight play, as a pantomime or even as a rhythmical interpretation with a record player or piano accompaniment.

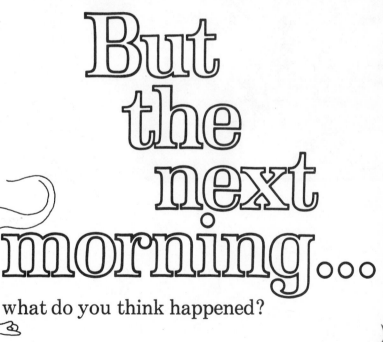

But the next morning…

what do you think happened?

Remember there is no right or wrong answer to this question.

Snow on the evergreen,
Happiness beckoning,
Children come caroling
Love to Mankind;

Here is another poetic excursion in open-endedness. The author
never does come out and TELL the reader it is Christmas. Thus
the children have the excitement of rolling the images around in
their minds and personally discovering that this could be Christmas. Whatever you do, don't ask what holiday it is. Let the children's discoveries come personally and without prompting. And if
the poem never does mean Christmas to some children, how
great. Poets don't like to be pinned down to exact meanings
anyway.

Garlands of mistletoe,
Candles and flowers glow,
Children come caroling
Love to Mankind.

Children Come Caroling

BY BILL MARTIN JR.
PAINTING BY CAROLYN JABLONSKY

Here is another in the sequence of "Indian" chants to be read against the others. The rhythm of this particular selection is keyed by reading *go go go go*, against the single word "beat" in the first selection.

GO GO GO   TEAM

GO TEAM   GETTUM TEAM

GO GO GO   TEAM

GO TEAM   GŁTTUM TEAM

SHUFFLE to the   *LEFT*

SHUFFLE SHUFFLE   SHUFFLE SHUFFLE

GO GO GO   TEAM

GO TEAM   GETTUM TEAM

CHEERLEADERS' CHANT

to be read like the beat of a tom-tom
by Bill Martin Jr.   lettering by Eric Carle

gettum gettum gettum TEAM

GO GETTUM *TEAM*

gettum gettum gettum TEAM

GO GETTUM *TEAM*

SHUFFLE to the LEFT

SHUFFLE to the *Left*

gettum gettum gettum TEAM

GO GETTUM *TEAM*

THE TREES ARE BARE, their leaves are off, I hope they're spared the whooping cough.

a verse

by Philip Keils

Two Tom Fooleries

Here are other concrete poems—the rhymes are
designed to suggest the content of the poem. The
poem below has the heavy shaggy look of a bear,
while the poem on the opposite page takes the
shape of a tree. Both of these poems are delightfully
nonsensical.

If you ever, ever, ever meet

a

Grizzly

Bear

You must never, never, never ask him where

He is going,

Or what he is doing;

For if you ever, ever dare

To stop a grizzly bear

You will never meet another grizzly bear.

by Mary Austin

MY FAVORITE BREAKFAST IS A FRIED EGG SANDWICH.

Breakfast

A STORY BY RED LANE,
PICTURES BY TIM AND GREG HILDEBRANDT

Don't be fearful that children will have difficulty reading this unusual type, and don't be surprised if you find some of them trying to write this way for decorative purposes.

MY FATHER'S FAVORITE BREAKFAST IS HAM AND EGGS.

Here is an interesting invitation to discussion and personal writing about likes and dislikes.

172

Here are worthwhile sentences for transforming.

MY DOG'S FAVORITE BREAKFAST IS PORRIDGE.

ONE MORNING
THERE WERE NO EGGS
FOR BREAKFAST
AND THERE WAS NO HAM
AND NO BREAD
FOR TOAST
AND NO JAM
AND NO
CEREAL FLAKES
AND NO
BROWN SUGAR

SO...

174

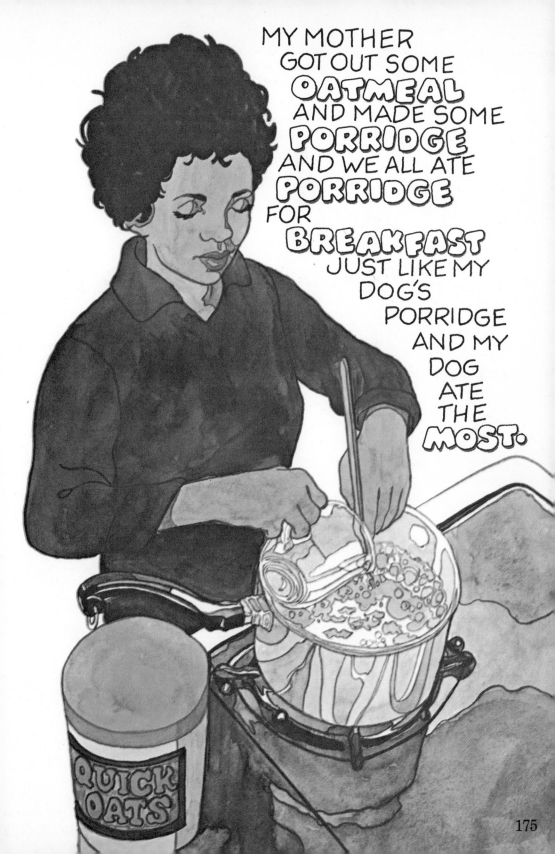

MY MOTHER GOT OUT SOME **OATMEAL** AND MADE SOME **PORRIDGE** AND WE ALL ATE **PORRIDGE** FOR **BREAKFAST** JUST LIKE MY DOG'S PORRIDGE AND MY DOG ATE THE **MOST.**

175

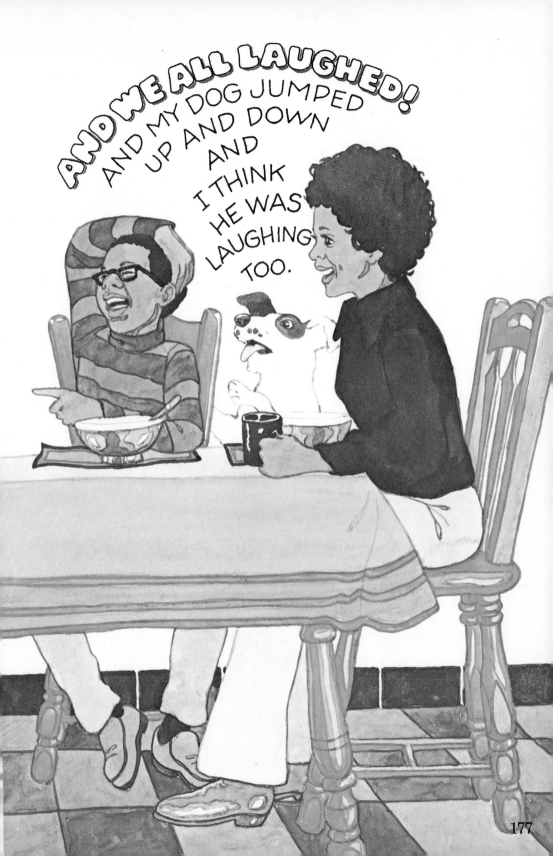

Do - re - mi - fa - so - la - ti - do . . .

DOE a deer, a female deer,

RAY a drop of golden sun,

ME a name I call myself,

FAR a long long way to run,

SEW a needle pulling thread,

LA a note to follow sew,

TEA a drink with jam and bread,

that will bring us back to . . .

...DO TI LA SO FA MI RE DO oh! - oh - oh - Do

a song from *The Sound of Music*, art by George Buckett. Copyright © 1956 by Richard Rodgers and Oscar Hammerstein 2nd. Used by permission of the publisher, Williamson Music, Inc.

Here's a Picture for Storytelling by E. W. Deming

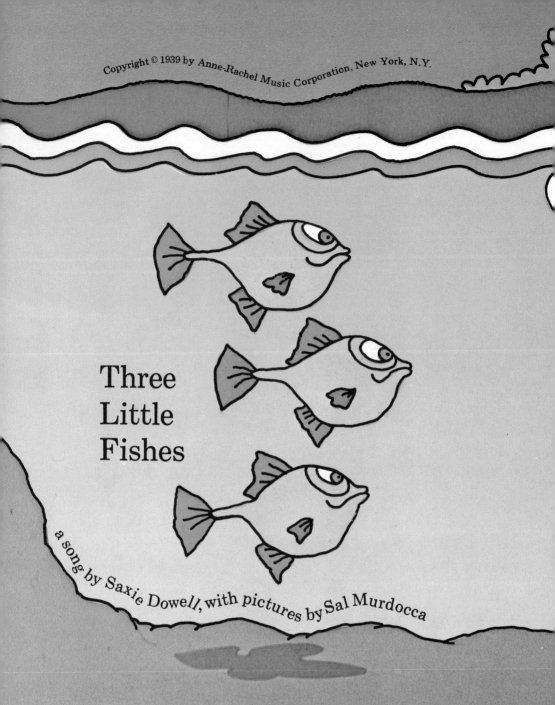

Three Little Fishes

a song by Saxie Dowell, with pictures by Sal Murdocca

Down in de meddy in a itty bitty poo,
Fam fee itty fitty and a mama fitty, foo.

This nonsensical story song of three little fishes, told in baby talk, follows the pattern of "Over in the Meadow" beginning on page 62. Children should have intimate familiarity with "Over in the Meadow" before they attempt to read this more complex story.

"Fim" fed de mama fitty,
"Fim if oo tan."
And dey fam and dey fam all over de dam.

Whenever children encounter a language that looks different from their own and they study it to figure out how it works, they gain insight into the fact that their own familiar language also has a system, one that they have been figuring out ever since they started to learn to talk and to read. Once the children's ears have heard the language in this selection their analytical activities will be well in progress. What fun they will have to figure out the system. Time and time again throughout the year you will probably refer to this experience as the children are deeply involved in analyzing some feature of the ordinary English language. Incidentally, this song provides functional phonics at its best!

"Top!" ted de mama fitty,
　　　　　"Or oo ill det ost."
De fee itty fitty dinna anna be bossed.
De fee itty fitty ent off on a spwee,
And dey fam and dey fam ight out to de fee.

"Whee!" 'elled de itty fitties,
"Ears a wot of fun,
Ee'll fim in de fee ill de day is un."
Dey fam and dey fam and it was a wark,
Till aw of a tudden dey taw a TARK!

"He'p!" tied de itty fitties,

    "Dee! ook at all de fales!"

And twit as dey tood dey turned on deir tails!

And bat to de poo in de meddy dey fam,

And dey fam and dey fam bat over de dam.

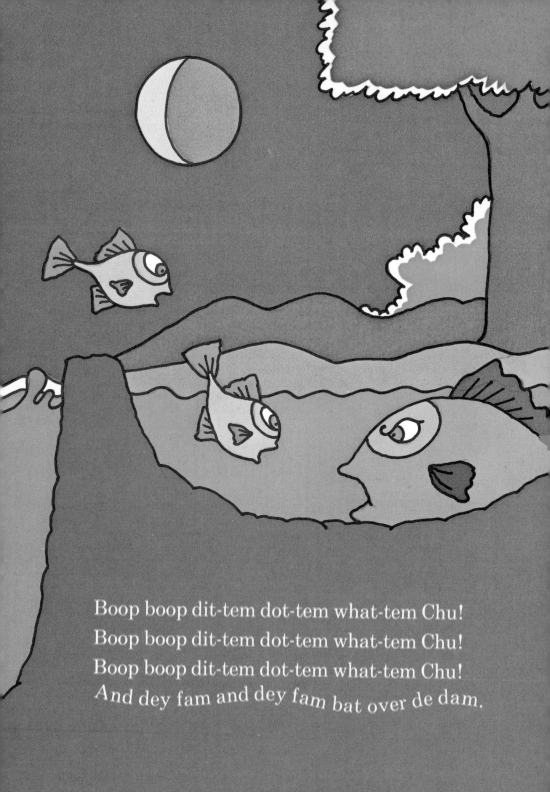

Boop boop dit-tem dot-tem what-tem Chu!
Boop boop dit-tem dot-tem what-tem Chu!
Boop boop dit-tem dot-tem what-tem Chu!
And dey fam and dey fam bat over de dam.

PUZZLE

Said   first   little   chicken

Cried		second	big	monkey
Roared	the	last	yellow	mother
Whispered		littlest	sassy	taxi-driver
Shouted		happiest	ugly	pumpkin
Wailed		meanest	spooky	ghost

queer

with   a

| funny |
| long |
| scary |
| silly |

How many different sentences can you make using this sentence for a pattern?

Here is a pictorial example of a sentence transformation. Encourage children to make up sentences that follow the original sentence pattern by selecting an innovation from each column of possibilities. When your children are suggesting vocabulary substitutions for their own sentence transforming, have you noticed how accurately they substitute nouns for nouns, verbs for verbs, etc.? This is part of their intuitive knowledge about language which they acquired by listening to the language when they were first learning to talk. In the SOUNDS OF LANGUAGE program we help children verbalize their intuitive knowledge and develop it into reading skills.

squirm,

little $\begin{bmatrix} \text{shrug} \\ \text{hop} \\ \text{smile} \\ \text{grunt} \\ \text{groan} \end{bmatrix}$

"I wish I could find a fat little worm."

$\begin{bmatrix} \text{I wish I could eat a fat little worm.} \\ \text{I wish I could scare all the children.} \\ \text{I wish I could warm my toes.} \\ \text{I wish I could give you a spanking.} \\ \text{I wish I could put you to bed.} \end{bmatrix}$

Jingle Bells

Jingle bells, jingle bells,
Jingle all the way,
Oh what fun it is to ride
In a one-horse open sleigh;
Jingle bells, jingle bells,
Jingle all the way,
Oh what fun it is to ride
In a one-horse open sleigh.

Where Are You Going, My Little Pig?

"I'm leaving my mother, I'm growing so big!"
"So big, young pig!
So young, so big!
Well, I never before saw a runaway pig!"

A JINGLE BY THOMAS HOOD,
DRAWINGS BY ALDREN WATSON

"Where are you going, my little pig?"
"I'm going to the barber's to buy me a wig!"
 "A wig, little pig!
 A pig in a wig!
Why, whoever before saw a pig in a wig?"

"Where are you going, my little pig?"
"I've got a spade, and I'm going to dig!"
    "To dig, little pig!
    A little pig dig!
Well, I never before saw a pig that could dig!"

196

"Where are you going, my little pig?"
"Why, I'm off to the ball to dance a fine jig!"
"A jig, little pig!
A pig dance a jig!
Well, I never before saw a pig dance a jig!"

This Old Man

He played one,
He played nicknack
on my thumb.
Nicknack paddywack,
Give the dog a bone!
This old man
came rolling home.

an old rhyme, pictures by Cornelio Martinez

Once again a childhood favorite. After children have the language, the rhythm, and the melody in their bones they will have no difficulty in responding to the clues that release the structure of the final verses.

This old man,
  He played two,
  He played nicknack
    on my shoe.
  Nicknack paddywhack
  Give the dog a bone!
  This old man
    came rolling home.

This old man,
 He played three,
 He played nicknack
  on my knee.
 Nicknack paddywhack
 Give the dog a bone!
 This old man
  came rolling home.

Now,

that you know

how this old rhyme goes

you can say the next seven verses

by knowing the two key words

in each verse:

You might ask the children, if they had never before seen the word "two," would they have any clue from the song itself that would help them know what the word is. They might suggest the clue given by the word *one* on the preceding page or they might suggest a rhyming clue from the word *shoe* on this page. Whatever their observations, praise the fact that they are growing in their ability to ferret out the ways an author has put his story or poem or song together. Remind them how much this skill will help them in their independent reading.

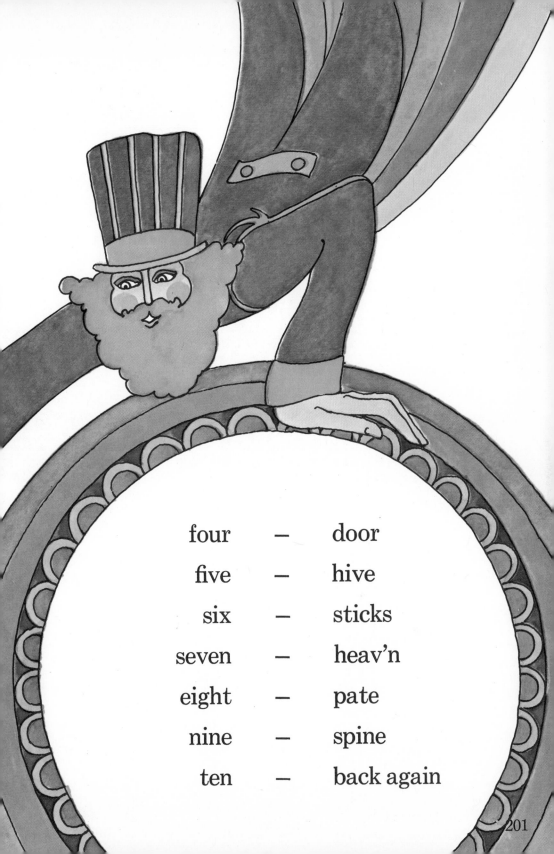

four	–	door
five	–	hive
six	–	sticks
seven	–	heav'n
eight	–	pate
nine	–	spine
ten	–	back again

Here is the last of the "Indian" chants. The key to this rhythm is in the pronouncing of the four-syllable word, *Mississippi*, to the timing of the word *beat* in the original poem. The children by now know that when they come to the phrasing "shuffle to the left," they have a clue as to whether their reading is synchronizing with the other chants. You and the children may enjoy knowing that the words "shuffle to the left" actually appear in Lew Sarett's majestic poem about Indians, "The Box of God."

MISSISSIPPI RIVER MORNING,
MISSISSIPPI RIVER WARNING,
MISSISSIPPI RIVER RAINING,
MISSISSIPPI RIVER WANING,

SHUFFLE to the LEFT

SHUFFLE SHUFFLE   SHUFFLE SHUFFLE

MISSISSIPPI RIVER MORNING,
MISSISSIPPI RIVER WARNING,

MISSISSIPPI RIVER CHANT

to be read like the beat of a tom-tom

by Bill Martin Jr.   lettering by Eric Carle

MISSISSIPPI SUN,
Thunder Wonder DONE,
MISSISSIPPI FLOOD,
OOZY NEWSY MUD,
SHUFFLE to the LEFT
SHUFFLE to the LEFT
MISSISSIPPI SUN,
Thunder Wonder DONE.

Maytime Magic

A little seed
For me to sow ...

A little earth
To make it grow ...

A little hole,

A little pat ...

A little wish,

And that is that.

A little sun,

A little shower ...

A little while,

And then—a flower!

A POEM BY MABEL WATTS

The Falling Star

I saw a star slide down the sky,

Blinding the north as it went by,

Too burning and too quick to hold,

Too lovely to be bought or sold,

Good only to make wishes on

And then forever to be gone.

A POEM BY SARA TEASDALE

PICTURES BY ED YOUNG

Here's a Picture for Storytelling by Dora Leder

209

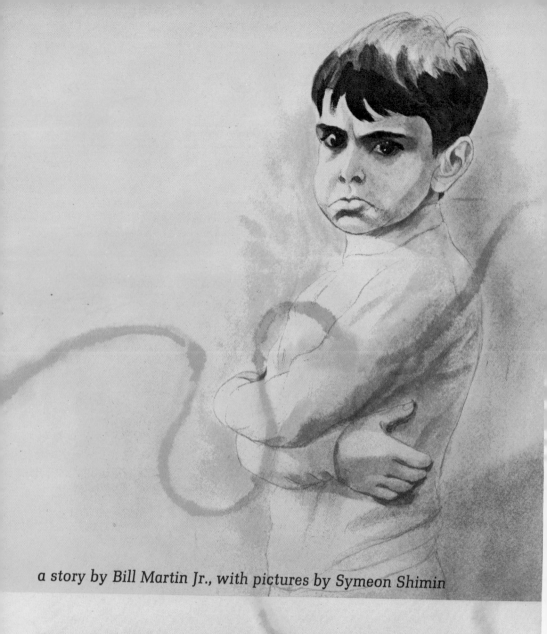

a story by Bill Martin Jr., with pictures by Symeon Shimin

DAVID WAS MAD!

This is a descriptive account of a boy's anger. It invites children to view their own periods of anger with objectivity, thereby helping them develop their own control. Anger is a natural part of the human experience. To deny a child his anger is to deny part of his wholeness. Anger in itself is not undesirable. Uncontrolled anger on the other hand breeds chaos, and that is to be avoided. How fortunate your children will be if in your objectivity you handle their periods of anger with the poise that the grandmother possesses in this story.

He was so angry that he kicked the wall
as hard as he could.
He felt hot—all RED inside.

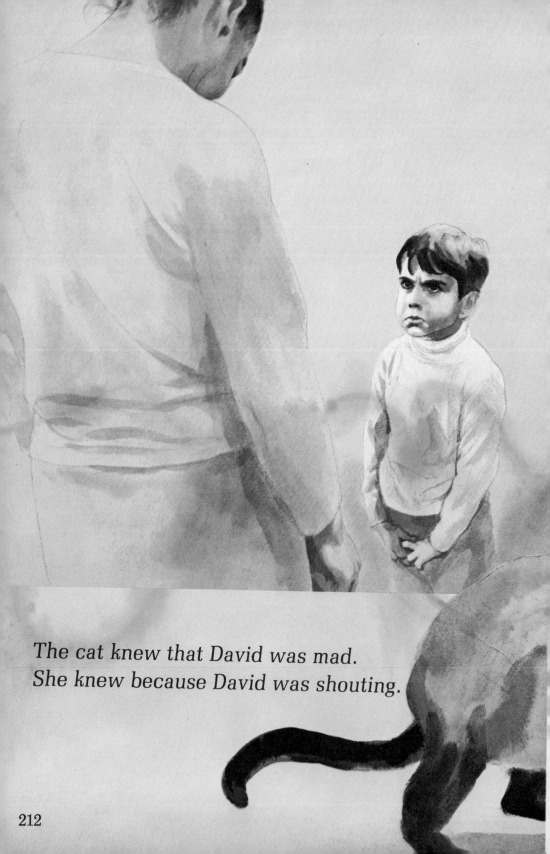

The cat knew that David was mad.
She knew because David was shouting.

Grandma knew that David was mad.
She knew because David was pouting.

Watch the children's faces as you read this
story, if you want a clear picture of the ex-
tent to which their life experiences help
them comprehend the fact that David was
mad.

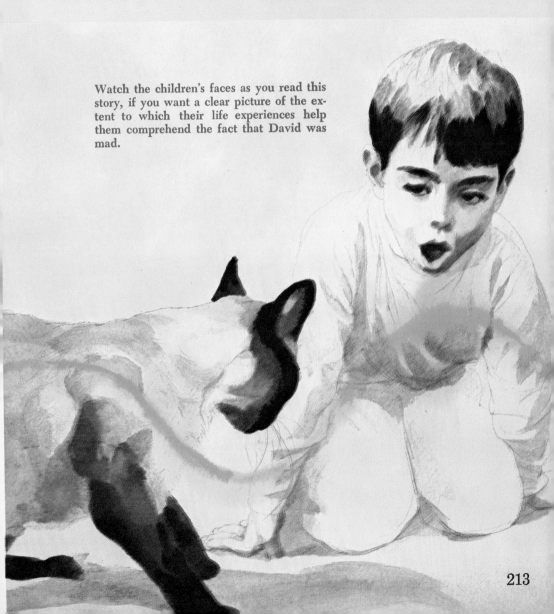

Sister knew that David was mad.
She knew because David hit her.

The teacher knew that David was mad.
She knew because David was scowling.

The children knew
that David was mad.
They knew because
David was arguing.

The children didn't like it,
and they began to argue.
Then they began to feel
all hot and RED inside.

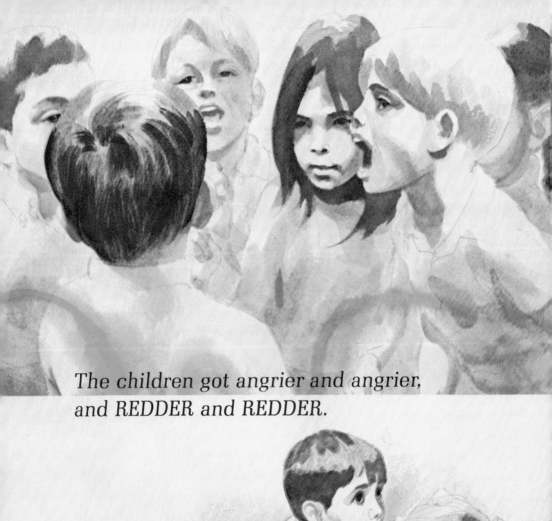

The children got angrier and angrier,
and REDDER and REDDER.

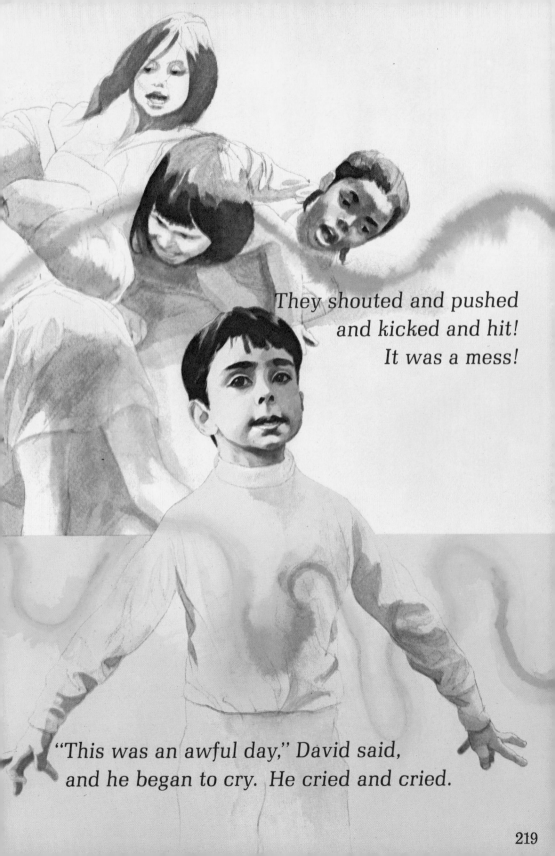

They shouted and pushed
and kicked and hit!
It was a mess!

"This was an awful day," David said,
and he began to cry. He cried and cried.

"I got mad first," David said,
"and then everybody else got mad."
"Yes, that's how it goes," Grandma said.
"Anger is like wet paint.
  It rubs off on everybody who touches it."

Symeon Shimin's sensitive and symbolic illustrations for this story deserve careful reading. The message of the story can be picture-read as well as word-read.

Already David was feeling better.
He was beginning to feel all sort of blue
and squishy inside.
His anger had passed.

My Love for You AN OLD JINGLE, ART BY GEORGE BUCKETT

I love you little, I love you lots;
My love for you would fill ten pots,
Fifteen buckets, sixteen cans,
Three teacups and four dishpans.

Navaho Happy Song

painting by Shaner

Read this Navaho song like a
chant with strong accents and
a lively rhythm.

Hi yo hi yo
Navajo
Navajo
Ip si ni yah
Ip si ni yah
Hi yo Navajo
Ip si *Ni* —
Yah!

A CHANT

SOUNDS OF LANGUAGE

Part One

The Heart of the Program

The *Sounds of Language* reading program
is a fresh and enchanting collection
of poems, stories, articles, and pictures
that realistically prompt children to hear the spoken patterns
of the sentences they read.
As children gain skill in using their ears
to guide their eyes in reading,
they have a qualitatively different reading experience.

little Indians, 4 little, 3 little, 2 little Indians, 1 little Indian boy. 1 little, 2 little, 3 little Indians, 4 little, 5 little, 6 little

Consider the young child
who has frequently heard his teacher read
"Ten Little Indians."
Once a child has these sounds
clearly and solidly in his ear,
he has little difficulty reading this old rhyme
in its printed form.
Once his ears begin telling him
what his eyes are seeing,
he approaches the reading with confidence and expectation.
And when he comes to his teacher and exultingly declares,

I know that word, Miss Barber!
That word is "little!"

she has evidence
that he is relating sight and sound in reading.
And it is easy for her to take this child a step further
by asking him if he can find the number 4,
or if he can find the word *Indian.*
It should not surprise you to know
that even at the first-grade level,
a child is already something of an expert
in analyzing language,
a fact overlooked in most reading programs.

You know, of course,
that we are referring to
both male and female teachers
when we use *he* throughout this essay.

Think of the three-year-old child on a bus
who says,

> *I rang the bell.*

a sentence sound he learned by listening.
At age four, he is apt to say,

> *I ringed the bell.*

a sentence sound that he never in his life heard.
Why then does he say it?
A child at four no longer simply imitates language sounds
that he hears in his environment.
He is beginning to figure out how language works
and how to make it work for him.
When he says, *I ringed the bell,*
he gives evidence that he is analyzing language
and that he knows how to change a verb
from present to past tense.

In similar ways in the *Sounds of Language* program,
a child is helped to become more and more expert in
using and analyzing language.
The aim is to help him become aware
of what he intuitively knows about language,
and to help him explore and verbalize
old and new learnings.

5 little, 6 little, 7 little Indians, 8 little, 9 little, 10 little Indian boys. 10 little Indians, 9 little, 8 little, 7 little, Indians,

—from *Sounds I Remember*

Language analysis emerges in abundance
at all levels in *Sounds of Language*
because the program is a total language and esthetic experience
which logically and comfortably connects a child
with his past experiences in using oral language
and with his intuitive knowledge of how language works.

Too many children in school have come to know reading
as word calling and drill,
with little or no opportunity
to claim language in its many dimensions.
The purposes of this teacher's edition, therefore,
are to help you join children and support them

1) in their growing appreciation of literature and language;

2) in a useful inquiry into how language works,
              both in its oral and written traditions;

3) in a useful inquiry into literary structure; and

4) in the development of esthetic awareness.

The pages of the pupil book (incorporated in this teacher's edition)
have been annotated for your convenience.
The annotations appear at the precise spot on the page
where they are needed to point up learning insights
and teaching strategies.

At no time is an annotation so prescriptive
that it precludes your insights from the teaching process.
To the contrary, the annotations are geared
to triggering all your insights and hunches
in helping children *latch on* to language and their humanity.

There is nothing complicated about this method of teaching.
Once you have read this informal dialogue
and the annotated pages,
you will feel comfortably at home with the program.
In fact, you may find yourself thinking:
Here, at last, is a program that helps me
use all of my knowledge and intuitions about language
—and about teaching.

Now, let's talk informally
       about ways for using the *Sounds of Language* readers
       to bring new dimensions
into your teaching of reading.
We have no choice but to help
all children learn to read.
They inherit the need to read
simply by living in our culture.
We, therefore, have the obligation to provide
wide-ranging ways for unlocking print.

What works for one child
doesn't necessarily work for another child.
What works for one kind of reading material
doesn't necessarily work for another.
Children are highly inventive and insightful
in ways of unlocking print—
until unimaginative reading instruction
tells them there is only one way to decode,
"Sound out the words!"
Actually, there are dozens of ways
to unlock the printed page.
And there are dozens of ways
that lead into the act of learning to read
before successfully pulling together
ear and eye and tongue and muscle
in the mature act of reading.

Some boys we have known
seemed at first to read more with their feet
than they did with their eyes.
You've had these kinds of boys
in your own classrooms.

Aren't they interesting
as they screw themselves up
into impossible positions
and keep perfect time to whatever is being read?
We should be saying to these boys:

> *Henry, you're so great at reading*
> *with your feet! How would you*
> *like to try reading with your eyes?*

And Henry wouldn't mind at all—
in fact he might be delighted to try—
knowing his comfortable way for responding to print
has been so respected.
But unfortunately,
we don't recognize Henry's rhythmical body response
as a reading behavior,
accustomed as we are to thinking about reading
as an eye exercise
and a "sounding-out" ritual.
Instead of praising Henry
and helping him include other parts of his body
in his response to the printed page,
we are likely to admonish:

> *Now, Henry, sit up straight*
> *and pay attention to your book.*

If Henry had the skill of self-analysis
and dared challenge the teacher's edict,
he might respond:

> *But I am paying attention.*
> *Rhythmical body response*
> *is part of reading a book.*

Only Henry doesn't have the language
for verbalizing his intuitive response to print.
And unless we have the awareness
to recognize what he is doing,
another potentially successful reader
will start the long and uncomfortable journey
of finding out that there is something wrong
with his way for learning to read;
and another potentially fine teacher
will be thrown into miscommunication with a child
simply because the definition of reading behavior
which has been made available to her
through teachers guides and college courses
is too narrow to accept and encourage
the many-faceted reading behaviors of real live children.

The *Sounds of Language* program makes it easy and enjoyable
for children and teachers to explore and perfect
multiple ways for unlocking print
and enjoying the miracle of language.
Children will learn to figure out the pattern
back of an author's way of putting a story
or poem or sentence together,
and to use this information for reading words
they didn't know they knew.
They will learn to figure out the different shapes of sentences
and to recognize unknown words
largely by where they fall in a sentence.
They will learn to figure out rhyme schemes and read new words
by recognizing where they fall in a certain rhyming slot.
They will learn to figure out underlying rhythmical patterns
and to use syllabic patterns
as one way to take hold of unknown words.

All of this, at first, may sound strange and complex
if you have not observed children using these natural ways
for making a go of reading.
But this essay will help you discover a multiplicity of ways
for using literature to bring new dimensions
into the teaching of reading.
The program is based on only a few practical teaching strategies.
These strategies work in kindergarten
as well as they work in eighth grade and all up and down the line.
The children themselves modify the strategies
by their individualized responses.

Once you own these strategies,
you can forget about the teacher's guide
and look forward to relaxed and creative reading sessions
where you are free to respond
to the children's individualized responses
and where you have a structural know-how
to help them learn to read.

The teaching strategies
explored in this essay are: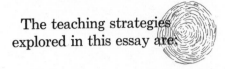

1) Recognizing That Language Works in Chunks of Meaning

2) Reading Aloud to Deposit Literary and Linguistic Structures
   in Children's Storehouses

3) Innovating on Literary Structure to Claim Basic Patterns

4) Figuring Out How Stories and Poems Work

5) Helping Children Verbalize Their Intuitive Literary Insights

6) Figuring Out How Sentences Work

7) Innovating on Sentence Patterns

8) Figuring Out How Words Work

9) Figuring Out How Print Works

10) Developing Skill in Comprehension

11) Linking Writing to Reading

12) Cultivating Literary and Esthetic Appreciation

13) Developing Sensitivity to the Three Levels of Language

14) Developing Sensitivity to Humanness

drawings from "My Mother is the Most Beautiful Woman in the World,"
Sounds of a Young Hunter

Learning to read
is not something that happens
after a stereotyped readiness period
in first grade or kindergarten.
Learning to read
is the job of a lifetime.
Two-and-three-year-old children who are read to a lot
begin their reading careers early.
The day a child gets hold of a sentence pattern that works for him
and reads it into the telephone directory
or the Montgomery Ward catalog
or his daddy's newspaper at night,
he is launching himself on his reading career.
He is role-playing himself as a successful reader.
The day a child reads a book from memory,
he is furthering his reading career.

He, in truth, is finding joy and power
in the pages of a book,
a psychological posture that every successful reader
continuously brings to each reading encounter,
knowing, subconsciously if not consciously,
that he can make a go of print.
This is the first and foremost reading skill.

Part Two

The Teaching Strategies for Sounds of Language

Whether it be at home or at school,
when children are read to,
they begin their naturalistic ways
for latching on to print
and they continue to expand and refine these ways
throughout the course of a lifetime—
provided they are given helpful opportunities.
The *Sounds of Language* teaching strategies
will help you provide these opportunities
for children to respond to print
in naturalistic intuitive ways;
and they also will help you release children
to verbalizing their intuitive responses to language and print,
and develop them into word-unlocking skills.

1 RECOGNIZING THAT LANGUAGE WORKS IN CHUNKS OF MEANING

As each of us learned to speak the language,
simply by imitating the speech sounds that we heard,
we learned to cluster words into meaningful units within a sentence.
Even as babies using nonsense syllables,
we used intonation and clustering
to create a *sound of sense*.
Later as we learned vocabulary and sentence ways,
we made full use of sentence sounds (sometimes called melodies)
demonstrating that we intuitively understood
that language works in chunks of meaning.
Not once did we isolate the word sounds
from the sentence sound in which they were cast.
Not one of us said,

> "*I* (pause) *want* (pause) *my* (pause) *mommy!*".

Rather "*Iwanmymommy!*"
came out as a meaningful linguistic whole,
a fluid sentence sound with a cultural melody
that conveyed both feeling and thought.
Unfortunately, language instruction in schools
has ignored the natural workings of language
by such unnatural techniques as

A) focusing word recognition skills on individual words
    rather than on the clustering of words within a sentence,

B) insisting on paragraph forms
    with rigid right-left hand margins that ignore
    the natural grouping of words within a sentence,

C) talking about word meaning as if a word
    actually has a meaning outside the context of the
    sentence in which it derived its meaning; and,

D) insisting that children in all of their school language activities
    perpetuate these misconceptions.

The poets, more than anyone else in our society,
have tended to improve
the communication potential of their writing
by arranging their words into natural linguistic clusterings.

All of us are familiar with the ragged right hand margin of a poem
and may never have stopped to think
why the sentences are written this way.
Just observe how Margaret Wise Brown
accommodates the lines in "Four Fur Feet"
to the chunks of meaning within each sentence:

OH, he walked along the river

on his four fur feet,

his four fur feet,

his four fur feet.

He walked along the river

on his four fur feet

and heard the boats go toot—O.

—*Sounds of a Powwow*

How different this is from a page of prose in an ordinary book
where each line must move rigidly
from a left hand margin to a right hand margin
with only the paragraph breaks
to give a feeling of structure to the printed language.
This inflexible technique cruelly severs words in half
in order to accommodate the margins,
as well as ignoring the natural clustering of words
into chunks of meaning within each sentence.
Let's see what a prose sentence would look like
if it were separated into its chunks of meaning
to enhance the linguistic design of the sentence
rather than the arbitrary width of the page.

> *I looked up*
>
> *with the water running off my face*
>
> *and saw a butterfly,*
>
> *bouncing from blossom to blossom*
>
> *like butterflies do.*

> —"Oh, Lord, I Wish I Was a Buzzard," *Sounds in the Wind*

As you observed, this is a complex sentence to read
but how much easier it becomes
when it is printed in its chunks of meaning.
Each of these groups of words has a meaning
that is more important than any single word within the group.
The words in each group, therefore, must be read together
as a subset of the more important set, the sentence.
Each subset leads into the next,
gradually amalgamating into the whole meaning of the sentence.
One of the miracles of our language
is its way of working in chunks of meaning.

An experienced reader does not move through a sentence
by reading each word separately.
Even though language is not ordinarily printed in chunks of meaning,
he learns to see—and sense—the groups of words
that best create meaning.
When a sentence is written from margin to margin across a column or
a page, with no special emphasis on the chunks of meaning, the reader
must do the work of seeing the words in clusters that release meaning.

This, at first, is not an easy task, but it is rewarding
because, soon, the reader finds himself
able to manage material that ordinarily would have stopped him.
Consider the problem of an inexperienced reader
who breaks a sentence into malfunctioning units, like this:

1) *Ayee, Mother do*

2) *not leave*

3) *us, for*

4) *we have*

5) *formed a chain and you*

6) *are the clasp that binds us.*

—"The Grandmother," *Sounds Jubilee*

Such a child has a comprehension problem immediately
because he has violated the linguistic units within the sentence.
Just try reading the sentence orally as it is grouped here
and you will shudder at the absence of the sound of sense.
*The only criterion for knowing a chunk of meaning when you see it
is to hear it.*
A child's intuition about language,
once he has developed the concept of chunks of meaning,
will lead him through the sentence this way,
simply because this is the way he would speak it
and thereby exploit its sound of sense:

1) *Ayee, Mother, do not leave us,*

2) *for we have formed a chain*

3) *and you are the clasp that binds us.*

Recognizing That Language Works in Chunks of Meaning TE 15

Reading instruction that emphasizes single word recognition
above all else
actually creates reading problems for children
because units of meaning are torn rudely apart
and children are not freed
to use their accumulated linguistic insights.
The concept of chunks of meaning within a sentence
is not foreign to children,
because they naturally speak in chunks of meaning
as they frame their oral sentences.
They need only to be helped to see that they can recreate
these same chunks on the printed page,
even if books are not printed in this way.
Hopefully the day will come when books,
at least for elementary school children,
will have considerable material printed in spoken language patterns.

2 READING ALOUD TO DEPOSIT LITERARY AND LINGUISTIC STRUCTURES IN CHILDREN'S STOREHOUSES

Each of us has a linguistic storehouse
into which we deposit patterns
for stories and poems and sentences and words.
These patterns enter through the ear
and remain available throughout the course of a lifetime
for reading and writing and speaking.
The good reader is a person who looks at a page of print
and begins triggering patterns
that have been stored in his linguistic treasury.
These patterns range all the way
from the plot structure an author has used in a story
to the rhyme scheme that hangs a poem together,
to the placement of an adjective in front of a noun
as part of the shape of a sentence,
to the underlying rhythmical structure in a line of prose or poetry,
to the *ed* ending as part of the shape of a word.

As these various kinds of structures
are brought into play
as a result of encountering a new version
of the same old basic structure,
a child is able to figure out much of the new vocabulary
because he recognizes the similarity
between the new structure
and structures he has already claimed.
A poor reader is the person who looks at a page of print
and no patterns are triggered to help him unlock the page.
This can be because he has not been read or talked to very much
and therefore has not deposited
story and poem and sentence and word patterns
in his linguistic storehouse.
Or this lack of triggering can occur
even if he has been talked to a lot
if the oral language patterns are not the kind
he is encountering in print.
A Spanish-speaking child, for example,
has stored sentence patterns
where the adjective follows the noun.
This does not help him unlock English sentences
where the adjective precedes the noun.
He will first have to hear and store in his being
the typical shape of English sentences
before his linguistic storehouse can help him unlock English print.

Now you can see why reading aloud
the poems and stories in the *Sounds of Language* readers
is a continuing part of this reading program
for children of all ages throughout their school years.
Sometimes you are reading aloud and the children are listening,
sometimes you are reading aloud and the children are chiming in,
sometimes the children are reading in chorus,
sometimes the boys and girls are reading aloud in dialogue,
sometimes the children are chorusing a poem or story by memory,
sometimes you and the children are reading aloud together,
with the children following the print in their books
so their eyes can be seeing what their ears are hearing
what their tongues are saying.

Dust
of Snow

The   way a crow
Shook down on me
The dust of snow
From a hemlock tree

Has given my heart
A change of mood
And saved some part
Of a day I had rued.

—"Dust of Snow" by Robert Frost, from *Sounds of a Young Hunter*

For example, a child who has heard frequently
and later read and chorused aloud "Dust of Snow,"
will have deposited within his linguistic treasury
a feeling for the sound and meaning of the word *rued*
that enhances his potential use of the word
in all kinds of communication—
reading, writing, speaking and listening.
He also will have a reservoir of potential
for shaping a sentence with the expertise
of this sentence shaped by a poet.
There is no better way for children to learn
to appreciate and use our language
than having broad and continuous experiences
that attune both the ear and the tongue—then later the eye—
to the rhythms, melodies and sounds of language.

Hopefully this reading aloud and language consolidation
will be accompanied by spontaneous body movement—
either the kind of swaying and clapping and shuffling
that children initiate on their own
or interesting movements suggested by you.
Whenever children engage their entire bodies
in their responses to print,
they have the best possible chance
to bring wholeness to the reading act
and intaking linguistic know-how.

3 INNOVATING ON LITERARY STRUCTURE TO CLAIM BASIC PATTERNS

One choice in deciding how to follow-up
your reading aloud of a story or poem
is to invite the children to utilize the author's pattern
for expressing their own thoughts.
By borrowing the underlying structure
of a poem or story or sentence that they have come to know,
they are involved in two linguistically sound learnings
as they hang their own ideas on that structure:

1) they are having intuitive experiences
    with the fact that stories and poems
    do have underlying structures,

2) they are building a bridge between
    the linguistic facts of their worlds
    and the linguistic facts of the printed page.

The invitation to "Write about anything you want to"
may fall heavily on the ears of a child
who doesn't own the basic language structures
to give wings to what he wants to say.

On the other hand, a child of seemingly meager vocabulary
can latch onto a structure that comes in through his ears
and deposits itself indelibly in his mind,
and suddenly find his vocabulary taking on new strength.

Christmas 1969

And lo it came to be
that she bore an infant
in the subway. Because
the apartment cost was
too high. She wrapped
him in paper towels
from a gas station. And
lay him on the cold walk-
way. The train rattled
by but no sound came
from him.

And it came to be
that friends heard of him
and came to see him.
They brought with them
gifts of grape drink, cigar-
ettes, and a few dollars.

—Kevin Clark, grade 6, Issaquah Valley School, Issaquah, Washington.

The *Sounds of Language* readers
make it possible for children of either rich or meager vocabulary
to find challenge in their new creations which come about
as they innovate on the dependable structures found in these books.
Your reading table may come alive
with fifteen new books (written by children)
each time you read a story or poem
and invite the children to borrow the structure
and to adorn it with their own thoughts and language.
What a wonderful source of material the reading table becomes
for the children's independent reading.
Since all of the innovative books
are built on structures which the children have already claimed
in read-aloud times with the *Sounds of Language* books,
the children will not only be able to read the new books more easily,
but they will be recognizing how useful

a person's knowledge about underlying structure
can be in helping him read.
Thus, children who have just finished reading:

Good night, Mr. Beetle,
Good night, Mr. Fly,
Good night, Mrs. Ladybug,
The moon's in the sky.

Good night, Miss Kitten,
Good night, Mr. Pup,
I'll see you in the morning
When the sun comes up.

—Sounds of Home

will tend to feel that they are meeting
an old friend when they come upon a child's innovated story:

Merry Christmas, Mr. Beetle,
Merry Christmas, Mr. Fly,
Merry Christmas, Mrs. Lady Bug,
Santa's in the sky.

Merry Christmas, Miss Kitten,
Merry Christmas, Mr. Pup,
I'll see you Christmas morning
When I open presents up.

Innovating on Literary Structure TE 21

Once the children have latched on to this notion
of borrowing a favorite literary structure for their own creations,
you will have many surprises in store.
Suddenly all of children's linguistic storehouse treasures
become available to them—
structures they have claimed both in and out of school—
and they begin to appear in the children's writing.
Imagine the surprise and delight of a fifth-grade teacher
who had asked his children to do a piece of writing
that would cause him to see pictures,
when a boy who had been considered an academic dropout
came up with this piece of writing:

The Frog

The frog in the pond a lony *(lonely)*
little fellow who lives with
the pussy wilow and the muss *(moss)*
who sits on a lilly like a bud wathing *(watching)*
the ixcitment of the day
when he sees a giant much bigger
than his size. He sits riady
coilled like a spring with bright
marrbled eys ready to dive
in the water and hid *(hide)* only to
disapear like mggic *(magic)* disgased *(disguised)*
with the polution of a once
lively and active pond.

—from Mr. Bredahl's sixth grade,
Roosevelt School, Minot, North Dakota

Where did the writing come from?
It has the ring of a poet,
yet the child obviously didn't copy it from print
for a poet would have grouped the words
into spoken speech units which this writing partially lacks.
Is this something this child heard
and deposited whole in his linguistic storehouse
and is now utilizing?
Or is it a combination of his own phrasing
and literary language he has stored?
The miracle is how beautifully and accurately
this boy has called upon his language storehouse
to fulfill his class assignment.
Luckily, this teacher did not feel
that it was *cheating* or *copying* or *uncreative*
to borrow literary lines and/or structure.
This is how a newcomer creates a language of depth and beauty.
Gradually he will transform and in other ways reshape
the language he has borrowed.
Meanwhile, in his borrowing,
he is role-playing himself as a distinguished user of language
and is tuning his ears to the beauty of speech.

Bruce's teacher experienced all of the wonder and surprise
of a genuine literary encounter
when she discovered these lines he had written:

> *Mystery of Bill Martin*
> *True blue surprise rubbed over man's flat eyes*
> *Truthful innocence scattered down Skinny's rectangular nose*
> —from Tucson Public Schools, class and grade unknown

Obviously Bruce has a well-stocked linguistic storehouse
and in self-selected ways he is experimenting
with combinations of words that please him,
albeit the sentence meanings are obtuse.

4 FIGURING OUT HOW STORIES AND POEMS WORK

Children like to figure out how things work.
From their earliest days
they are endlessly poking and pushing and pulling-apart
to find out what makes things go.
This is how they learned to talk.
They listened to the talk on all sides of them
and they began experimenting and figuring out how talk works.
Once they began to figure out what they needed to know,
they made talk work for them.

In a similar way,
when you read a highly structured story to children,
they will chime in with you long before you have finished the story:

Brown bear, brown bear,

what do you see?

I see a redbird

looking at me.

**Redbird, redbird,
what do you see?**

**I see a yellow duck
looking at me.** [1]

As you turn the page and the children burst out reading

**Yellow duck, yellow duck,
what do you see?**

knowing, without even looking at the print, how the story is working,
they are giving evidence
that they have not simply memorized the story.
They have figured out how the author put his story together
and they are using this information
to help them read pages you haven't even read to them yet.
Much of this kind of figuring-out is intuitive.
It goes on while you are reading aloud
and while the children are chiming the story along with you.
Your job is to help the children verbalize these intuitive insights
and to organize them into word-unlocking skills.
Knowing how stories and poems are put together
will therefore be a help both to you and the children.
To begin with, stories are a series of episodes
or happenings arranged in some kind of recognizable shape.
For our purposes we view an episode
as either an action within a series of actions
or a language pattern within a series of related language patterns.
In so far as possible, in designing the early *Sounds of Language* readers,
we have used the turning of the page to indicate a new episode.

[1] This story by Bill Martin appears
both in the *Kin/der Owls* and in the Level 1 *Instant Readers*.

A)   Repetitive Sequence

In some stories, the episodes repeat one another.
We have called that kind of story structure *repetitive sequence.*

My name is Tommy.
I am not very big.

I am not as big as a goat.   EPISODE 1
A goat is bigger than I am.

I am not as big as a horse.   EPISODE 2
A horse is bigger than I am.

I am not as big as an elephant.   EPISODE 3
An elephant is bigger than I am.

I am not as big as a whale.   EPISODE 4
A whale is bigger than I am.

I am not as big as a dinosaur.
EPISODE 5
A dinosaur is the
biggest thing I know.

—from "What Is Big?" *Sounds of Numbers*

Even on first acquaintance, a child will predict

   1) that the pattern of phrasing will maintain,

   2) that all of the creatures will be described as big/bigger,

   3) that in each comparison, the last part of the first sentence
      becomes the first part of the second sentence.

When the children come to the last episode, numbered 5,
and the repetitive pattern breaks,
we have dramatically enlarged the new language pattern
to signal to the children that something has changed
and the repetition has stopped.
The enlarged type also is a semantic clue
that tends to trigger children
into use of the superlative form of the adjective *big*,
which in its own way
also signals the end of the comparative sequence.
These kinds of exaggerated clues help children learn to trust print,
knowing that an author will keep leaving visual clues
that help the reader decode.
Imagine a child's surprise, therefore,
to discover that the dinosaur is not *bigger than I am*
but is *the biggest thing I know.*
Couched as this variation is within so many dependable repetitions,
it does not cause a child to lose faith in structural repetitions,
but rather it invites him to develop another literary insight—
that when a repetitive pattern gets going,
the author will at some time break the pattern
in order to bring the story to an end.
His curiosity is, therefore, piqued
to predict ways the author can break a repetitive pattern.

Let's look at another example:

Round is a pancake,   EPISODE 1
Round is a plum,   EPISODE 2
Round is a doughnut,   EPISODE 3
Round is a drum.   EPISODE 4

Round is a puppy   EPISODE 5
    Curled up on a rug.
Round are the spots   EPISODE 6
    On a wee ladybug.

Here is the
pattern break
signalling
that the   Look all around,   EPISODE 7
story is
ending.   On the ground, in the air,
You will find round things
Everywhere.

—from *Sounds of Home*

Although episodes 5 and 6 are patterned extensions
of the previous episodes,
the reliability of their beginning phrases
cues the children to predict
that they can make a go
of a somewhat different sentence.
And, when the children come to the last episode, number 7,
and it does not begin with the repeated phrase *Round is,*
they have a reliable clue for predicting
that this repetitive story is coming to an end.

And here's a repetitive pattern
that's worn smooth with a lifetime of continuations:

As wet as a 🐟 — as dry as a bone;

As live as a bird — as dead as a stone;

As plump as a partridge — as poor as a rat;

As strong as a 🐎 — as weak as a 🐱 ;

As hard as a flint — as soft as a mole;

As white as a lily — as black as a coal;

As plain as a staff — as rough as a 🐻 ;

As tight as a 🥁 — as free as the air;

As heavy as lead — as light as a 🪶 ;

As steady as time — as uncertain as weather;

As hot as an oven — as cold as a 🐸 ;

As gay as a lark — as sick as a 🐕 ;

As savage as tigers — as mild as a dove;

As stiff as a poker — as limp as a 🧤 ;

As blind as a bat — as deaf as a post;

As cool as a 🥒 — as warm as toast;

As blunt as a 🔨 — as sharp as an awl;

As flat as a flounder — as round as a ⚽ ;

As brittle as glass — as tough as gristle;

As neat as a pin — as clean as a 🦴 ;

As red as a 🌹 — as square as a box;

As bold as a thief — as sly as a 🦊 .

—from *Sounds of Mystery*

While most stories have more than one kind of pattern
in their make-up,
many of the *Sounds of Language* selections
have enough obvious repetitions in their underlying structures
that children are propelled into anticipating the next line or episode.
Naturally this is not an infallible method
of decoding print,
but it is highly useful in combination with
the many other decoding skills
which are developed in the *Sounds of Language* program.
Moreover, it releases children to a continuous flow of reading
without the traditional vocabulary breakdowns
that are engendered by word-by-word reading
and which rob the language of its melodies and structural rhythms.
Children enjoy the *aha!* feeling which comes
when they predict that the second and third billy goats[2]
will behave much the same as the first billy goat
and when they predict that much of the language (and action)
in the first episode will be repeated.
They feel that they have a successful hold on the story
in "The Three Little Pigs and the Ogre"[3]

when the first little pig outwits the ogre
and they predict that the other two pigs
will try to do the same.
When children make identification with a strong character,
such as Ol' Stormalong,[4] they will predict
that even when he turns into a cowboy and a farmer,
much of his talk and actions
will repeat the talk and actions of Ol' Stormalong, the sailor.
Once you are aware
that a repetitive sequence is one way
of arranging the happenings in a story,
you probably will think of many other stories
which are arranged in this style.
You probably will also remember
how easily the children were able
to take hold of those stories
when you read them aloud.
At the time, you may not have realized
that the children were not simply memorizing—
that they were responding to the reliable repetition
in the story structure.

"Blo-o-ows!
Thar she blows!"

Swoosh!

"Hooray, a storm!" shouted Stormalong to the farmers.
"Now I can get the kinks out of my muscles.
Avast there, mateys! Storm ahead! All hands on deck!"

"Just sit down and rest yourselves,
me hearties," said Stormalong.
"I'll round 'em up,
just to get the kinks out of my muscles."

[2] "The Three Billy Goats Gruff," *Sounds of Laughter*

[3] *Sounds of Mystery*

[4] "How Ol' Stormalong Captured Mocha Dick," *Sounds of a Distant Drum*

Figuring Out How Stories and Poems Work TE 31

This is the house
   that Jack built.
This is the malt,
That lay in the house
   that Jack built.
This is the RAT
That ate the malt,
That lay in the house
   that Jack built.

—from *Sounds Around the Clock*

How pleasantly this old cumulative rhyme
falls into place.
Each new line (episode) adds a new thought
before repeating everything that went before.
Children who sense the cumulative nature of this story
have a lot going for them.
They know, for example, that all of each subsequent page
will be familiar to them
except for the one added thought.
They also know that each new page will have more type
than the preceding page
and that they will be able to easily read
this accumulating language because it is familiar.
Children, on the other hand,
who are taught to read word by word,
are often turned away from pages with a lot of type
because they do not have structural insights
to help them unravel the print.

Throughout *Sounds of Language* children will encounter
stories and poems and songs and jingles
put together with a cumulative structure.
Each new encounter will remind them
that their insight into new selections
is influenced by the fact
that the basic pattern of cumulative writing
has already been deposited in their linguistic storehouses
and is now available for a lifetime of use
in reading and writing and literary appreciation.

Just for fun, let's see at which point you sense
that "I Came to this Land"
is cumulative in structure.

> *When I first came to this land,*
> > *I was not a wealthy man,*
> *Then I built myself a shack.*
> > *I did what I eould.*
> *I called my shack, Break-my-back.*
> *Still the land was sweet and good,*
> > *I did what I could.*
>
> *When I first came to this land,*
> > *I was not a wealthy man,*
> *Then I bought myself a cow.*
> > *I did what I could.*
> *I called my cow, No-milk-now,*
> *I called my shack, Break-my-back.*
> *Still the land was sweet and good.*
> > *I did what I could.*
>
> —from "I Came to this Land," *Sounds Jubilee*

Up until the line in the second verse,
"*I called my shack, Break-my-back,*"
this structure obviously is repetitive,
but the use of this particular line in sequence with the new episode
is evidence for predicting
that this is both a repetitive and cumulative sequence,
and that each new episode will include
an accumulation of the man's previously named possessions.

Figuring Out How Stories and Poems Work TE 33

Thus, you can figure out all six verses of this story song
with just the following information:

> *I bought myself a horse,*
> *I called my horse, Lame-of-course.*
>
> *I bought myself a duck,*
> *I called my duck, Out-of-luck.*

Aha! Now you're sensing that each creature's given name
is rhyming with the categorical name of the creature—
another structural clue.
Now you have three kinds of literary structure
going for you—repetitive, cumulative and rhyme-rhythm.

> *I got myself a wife,*
> *I called my wife, Joy-of-life.*
>
> *I got myself a son,*
> *I told my son, "My work's done."*

Aha! The author now has broken the language repetition,
signalling that he has probably reached the conclusion of his story.
Observe the additional semantic shift
in the first word of the last chorus:

> **For** *the land was sweet and good,*
> *I did what I could.*

This indeed confirms the fact that the story is over.
Did you enjoy getting hold of the story
partly by recognizing how the author put it together?
That same *aha!* feeling of awareness
that came to you as you figured out the pattern
and then made the pattern help you read the story successfully
is the same feeling that children get
when they sense an author's plan.
At the end of this section on various types of literary structure,
you'll find suggestions
for helping children verbalize the *aha!* feeling
and developing it into a word-unlocking skill.

C) Interlocking Sequence

Sometimes the episodes in a story or poem or song
do not simply repeat or accumulate,
rather they interlock in an intriguing way.

> *The funny old man and the funny old woman*
>   *sat by the fire one night.*
> *"Funny old man," the old woman said,*
>   *"I don't know what to do.*
> *When I went to the barn to milk the cow,*
>   *the funny old cow wouldn't moo."*
>
> *The funny old man scratched his head,*
>   *"I know what to do," he said.*
> *"Take her to town to see Dr. Brown*
>   *and bring her home in the morning.*
> *That's what you do when the cow won't moo."*
>
> *"But she's out in the woodshed lying down.*
>   *How will you take the cow to town*
> *and bring her home in the morning?"*
>
> *"If she can't walk," said the funny old man,*
>   *"I'll push her in the wheelbarrow if I can*
> *and bring her home in the morning."*
>
> *"But the goat's asleep in the wheelbarrow.*
>   *Where shall I put the goat?"*
>
> *"Put the goat on top of the garden gate.*
>   *The goat can sleep there very late*
> *till the cow comes home in the morning."*
>
> *"But the rooster is roosting on the garden gate.*
>   *Where shall I put the rooster?"*
>
> *"Put the rooster in the butter churn,*
>   *so tight that he can't twist or turn*
> *till the cow comes home in the morning."*
>
> *"But . . ."*

—from "The Funny Old Man and the Funny Old Woman,"
Sounds of Laughter

Are you caught up in the intrigue
of this sequence, and ready to predict the

"But..." (says the old woman)

"Put..." (says the old man)

pattern on which this story is built?

Even if you had never learned
to sound out the word *butter*,
you are prepared to read this word in this story slot

"But my nice fresh butter is in the churn.

Where shall I put my butter?"

knowing how it interlocks with the preceding lines

"Put the rooster in the butter churn

so tight that he can't twist or turn

till the cow comes home in the morning."

Finally in this humorous story
when the old man says,

"Put the pig on a pillow in the feather bed,"

and the old woman says,

"No,"

instead of

"But,"

you know for sure that the interlocking pattern has been broken
and the story is coming to an end.

Now to exploit your structural know-how,
have a go at this:

I came to the river...

and I couldn't get across,

I jumped on a frog 'cause I thought it was a hoss,

The hoss wouldn't pull so I traded for a bull,

The bull wouldn't holler so I sold him for a dollar,

The dollar wouldn't pass so I threw it in the grass,

The grass wouldn't grow so I traded for a hoe,

The hoe wouldn't dig so I traded for a pig,

_ __ __ squeal _ _ __ _ _ wheel,

_ __ __ run _ _ __ _ _ gun,

_ __ __ shoot _ _ __ _ _ boot,

_ __ __ fit _ _ thought I'd quit

And I did.

—an old rhyme, *Sounds of Mystery*

Think how much vocabulary is unlocked
simply by recognizing that these lines
interlock with one another
rather than simply follow one another.
You probably remember adult stories
where some happening triggered off
or brought together a chain of events,
such as in *The Bridge at San Luis Rey*
or Chaucer's *Canterbury Tales*.
Even the reading or viewing of Shakespearean plays
is both simplified and intensified
when you recognize the interlocking relationships
of characters.
The moment you con Lady Macbeth
or Claudius or Petruccio, for example,
you begin predicting events and language.
What a reading skill!

D) Familiar Cultural Sequences

Simply by living in our culture,
children have certain built-in structures going for them
that can be put to work in learning to read.
They know, for example, that the hours of the day,
the days of the week, the months and seasons,
the number system and the alphabet
have dependable sequences.
Sooner or later
children become familiar with and use these sequences
like another hand or foot or ear or eye
in dealing with the outside world.
The *Sounds of Language* program
exploits certain of these structures
as another way to help children appreciate the fact
that the recognition of underlying sequence
is an aid in decoding print:

In the first month of the year
I found one brown pony
and he followed me home.

In the second month of the year
I found two white kittens
and they followed me home.

—from "One, Two, Three, Four," Sounds of Numbers

Children are now prepared to read the words *third* and *three*
because they sense that along with the repetition
in this story
is a reliance on ordinal and cardinal numbers.
Similarly,

On Monday I make strong boxes...

   On Tuesday

   I make

   narrow boxes...

—from "A Maker of Boxes," Sounds of Laughter

children who have never seen the word *Wednesday*
anticipate that it will be used in the next episode,
and will read the word in its appropriate slot,
confirming the fact that they recognize
the author's basic way of organizing his story.
It's a proud triumph for a reader.

Seventh graders can enjoy unlocking print
by using a familiar cultural sequence (the alphabet)
that has been with them since nursery school days:

A you're adorable, **B**

you're so beautiful, **C** you're a

cutie full o' charms **D** you're a

darling, and **E** you're exciting,

and **F** you're a feather in my arms.

—from "A You're Adorable," *Sounds Jubilee*

Once you and the children recognize familiar cultural sequence
as the organizing factor in putting certain stories together,
you may wish to begin a bulletin-board collection
of such sequences.
And don't be surprised if the children list the count-down
as a sequence which is securely deposited
in their linguistic storehouses.

E) Chronological Sequence

Sometimes it is easy to hunch early in a story
that the episodes are arranged chronologically.
This kind of hunch gives the expectation
that the vocabulary will be influenced
by an ordering of events based on time.
Biographies and autobiographies
tend to work this way.
Very often detective stories
unfold in a time sequence.
Even in the old nursery rhyme when

*Jack and Jill went **up** the hill*

you expect them to come tumbling *down*.

Children are in the mood
for spanning the events of a lifetime
when they read:

This is Johnny.

He is a baby.

He cannot walk.

He cannot talk.

But he can cry!

Johnny is 1 week old.

Now Johnny can walk.

He laughs and claps his hands.

He says "dada" and "mama"

and "baby."

Johnny is 1 year old.

Now Johnny is 4 years old....

He is not a baby anymore....

Johnny is 6 years old now

He is in the first grade....

Now Johnny is 12.

He goes to junior high school....

—from "Growing Up, Growing Older,"
Sounds of Laughter

As children follow Johnny's life
through to his happy grandfather days,
they anticipate and soon are comfortable with lifetime words
such as *junior high school, young man, college,
home from the air force, wedding day.*
Even as they study the art for clues,
children have strong notions of what they are looking for
(such as signs of physical aging, and signs of maturity)
because of their recognition
of the chronological sequence on which the story hangs.

In even wider ranging applications
of this particular literary know-how,
children will create useful expectations
based on other kinds of chronological sequencing:

1) the logical ordering of events in a story,
   particularly a mystery story where the solution
   usually comes at the end:
   such as "The Ghostly Hitchhiker,"
   Sounds Freedomring

2) the ordering of events on a trip,
   be it a spaceflight or a picnic.

3) the shaping of events by weather patterns,
   i.e. "Snowbound," *Sounds of a Distant Drum*

4) explanatory sequences such as giving directions,
   i.e. "How to Brush Your Teeth," *Sounds of a Young Hunter*

F) Problem-Centered Sequence

The minute Mother Meadowlark awakens
with a snake curled about her nest,
there is no doubting that she has a problem.[5]
Whenever a main character in a story
is confronted with a crucial problem,
the person reading the story can predict
that one episode after another will occur
until the problem is solved.
Once the problem is solved
the reader does not expect the story to go on
for fifty more pages.
He knows that the story is finished.
There isn't that much more to talk about.
The episodes which occur in solving the problem
can be repetitive, cumulative,
interlocking or chronological.
They can also be arranged
around familiar cultural sequences.
In other words,
a story does not have only a basic shape.
It can also have shapes within shapes.
Children reading "The Billy Goats Gruff"[6]
soon recognize that the episodes which occur as the three goats
solve their problem with the troll
are repetitive.

[5] "Mother Meadowlark and Brother Snake," *Sounds of the Storyteller*
[6] *Sounds of Laughter*

The bridge goes,

"Trip, Trap! Trip, Trap! Trip, Trap!"

each time a goat crosses over.
The troll threatens each time.
The goats respond.
When the third goat breaks the repetitive pattern
and solves the problem,
the story comes to an end.
In their reading of the story,
children have two kinds of structural insight going for them:

1) the problem of the troll and its solution;

2) the repetition of action
    and vocabulary from episode to episode.

In "The Web of Winter"[7]
the main character encounters a problem
when he discovers a young duck unable to fly
because it is frozen in the ice.
From that point on, the episodes move chronologically.
As Bill frantically tries to free the bird
and the day moves toward night,
the children reading the story
are reaching out toward a solution.
And while the problem-centered, chronological structure
does not predict the exact language,
it does prepare the children to expect vocabulary
related to the efforts to save the duck,
to the actual saving of the duck,
to the passing time of day,
to the vocabulary associated with the passing time of day,
such as *suppertime, darkness, headlights,* etc.
and to certain character traits.
All of these linguistic insights
are germane to unlocking the print.

[7] *Sounds of Mystery*

Some poems and stories
are put together with a dependable rhyme-rhythm scheme.

The Owl and the Pussy-cat went to sea
In a beautiful pea-green boat:
They took some honey, and plenty of money
Wrapped up in a five-pound note.

—from "The Owl and the Pussy Cat," *Sounds After Dark*

You may have been taught
that this is an A-B-C-B rhyme-rhythm scheme,
meaning that the second and fourth lines rhyme
and the rhythm is predictable.
Heaven forbid that we lecture children
about the A-B-C-B rhyme-rhythm scheme!
But we can help them verbalize the fact
that when you have figured out
the author's rhyming-meter plan,
it is easier to read the rhyming words
and to syllabicate certain words
used in the rhyme-rhythm slots.

Slowly ticks the big clock;

Tick-tock, Tick-tock!

But Cuckoo clock ticks double quick;

Tick-a-tock-a, tick-a-tock-a,
Tick-a-tock-a, [   ] [8]

Do you find yourself supplying the word *tick*
to keep the rhyme scheme going?
This is how it is with response to rhyme scheme.

[8] "The Big Clock," *Sounds Around the Clock*

One way to help children verbalize
how useful a rhyme scheme can be
in recognizing vocabulary
is to read them a regularly patterned verse
and ask them to supply words you leave out.

Boys and girls, supposing you keep your books closed
while I read you an old rhyme.
I'm going to leave out some of the words
and you see if you can say those words
even though you've never heard the poem:

This is the story

Of Susie Moriar.

It started one night

As she sat by the ☐

The fire was so hot,

Susie jumped in a ☐

The pot was so black,

Susie dropped in a ☐

The crack was so narrow,

Susie climbed on a wheel☐

The wheelbarrow was so low,

Susie fell in the ☐

The snow was so white,

Susie stayed there all ☐

The night was so long,

Susie sang a ☐

—from "Susie Moriar," *Sounds of Laughter*

As the children supply the missing words,
they are responding to both the rhythmical and rhyming patterns
of this old jingle.
It is important to help them verbalize
their ways of figuring out the missing words
and to discuss the fact that
in their independent reading,
they can use this kind of structural insight
to figure out certain unknown vocabulary.
At some point in the discussion,
it can be useful to suggest:

> *Children, supposing you wanted*
> *to change the poem about Susie Moriar.*
> *Let's see where we can go with*
>
> *"This is the story of Jennie McGoo.*
> *It started one night as she ..."*

As the children pick up the aa-bb-cc, etc. scheme
of the original jingle
they may be suggesting:

> *This is the story of Jennie McGoo.*
> *It started one night as she went to the zoo.*
> *The zoo was so bright,*
> *Jennie stayed there all night ...*

Some children, however, may not respond
to the rhythm-rhyme scheme of the original jingle
and may come up with something like

> *This is the story of Jennie McGoo.*
> *It started one night as she went to sleep.*

When such a suggestion is made,
your role is to accept it positively
and help the children see the difference
between this and the original pattern.

Isn't this interesting, boys and girls?
Chuck has suggested a pattern
that doesn't rhyme the way the original poem did.
Let's follow Chuck's lead for awhile
and see where we go.

"This is the story of Jennie McGoo.
It started one night as she fell asleep.
Next thing she knew she was floating on a cloud . . ."

And so develops an innovation
that is patterned on story ideas
rather than the original rhyme scheme.
Both kinds of innovating are important.
As the children discuss differences
between rhyming and non-rhyming patterns,
they will further appreciate how recognition
of a rhythm-rhyme scheme
helps a person unlock unknown vocabulary.

Obviously there are other and more subtle literary structures
such as a story like "Old Lucy Lindy"[9]
and "Yallery Brown"[10]
in which the episodes hang on character development
but for purposes of this discussion
we have confined ourselves to those story patterns
which are most productive
in helping children predict language
and thereby unlock vocabulary.

In all of this discussion
of ways for putting stories and poems together,
we have been faced with the interesting fact
that whenever many of anything come together,
be they objects or events or words or people,
they either fall together helter-skelter
or they fall into an arrangement of some kind.
An earthquake produces hit-and-miss.
Language, whatever else, creates order.

[9] *Sounds of the Storyteller*
[10] *Sounds Freedomring*

48 TE Figuring Out How Stories and Poems Work

When children are helped to verbalize
their recognition of the various ways
authors can arrange episodes in a story or poem,
they develop a reading skill
that forever lifts them out of the
little-steps-for-little-feet way of viewing a book.
A book or story or poem, whatever else it is,
is not a succession of isolated words
to be sounded out
or an unmanageable succession
of disassociated thoughts and events.
Traditional "basic" reading and language instructions
are not "basic" in the least
unless they include opportunities
for children to develop their naturalistic and intuitive skills
in unlocking the flow of language
in its basic cultural patterns.
It's as important for a child to know
how a piece of writing is unfolding
as it is for him to know
how a word unlocks.
The joyful fact is
that as a child takes root and strength
in his abilities to anticipate literary structure,
he, simultaneously, is developing word-unlocking skills
that save him from being stranded
with "sounding out" as the only way
to manage unknown words.

5 HELPING CHILDREN VERBALIZE THEIR INTUITIVE LITERARY INSIGHTS

You may be wondering
how to help children
verbalize their structural insights.
Actually, your discussion with the children
occurs all along the line.

If the children quickly chime in
during your first reading of a story,
you may wish to engage them in easy conversation
about their ease in chiming in.

> *How come you children were able to read*
> *so much of that story*
> *without hearing it first?*

Their homely explanations will tell you
whether or not they are using
the structure of the story
as one of their ways for unlocking print.

> *When he said, "I'm not as big as a goat"*
> *and "I'm not as big as a horse,"*
> *I knew he was going to keep on saying*
> *"I'm not as big as a . . . . ."*

This is a young child's natural way for telling you
that he is beginning to recognize repetitive sequence.

> *How does it happen you children*
> *read that word* Wednesday *so easily?*

> *"Well, when the author said*
> *'On Monday I build . . .' and*
> *then when he said, 'On Tuesday*
> *I build . . .' I knew he was going*
> *to say, 'On Wednesday . . .' "*

Here a child is verbalizing his awareness
of structure built on familiar cultural sequences.

Isn't it interesting, children,
when you figure out how an
author put his story together,
it helps you in your reading.

This kind of remark will help children
generalize their experience in the use of literary structure
to unlock print.
It also helps give them the vocabulary
for verbalizing what they have experienced.
A word of caution:
generalizing statements of this kind do not come
before the children have had the experience
of successfully using story or poem structure
to make their reading easier.
If the generalizations are to be the children's—
and they must be the children's
if they are to become part
of their personal collection
of word-unlocking skills—
they must grow out of first-hand experiences.
When they do grow out of first-hand experiences,
the children will claim the generalizations as their own,
depositing them in their linguistic storehouses
for future reference.
If the children are reading independently
and can recognize words
with or without help from literary structure,
you may wish to come at your questioning
from a different angle.

Children, supposing you had never seen
the word Wednesday (or any other word
that can be anticipated
by knowing the structural sequence of the story).
Is there anything in this story
that gives you a hint
that could help you read the word?

This kind of questioning may lead
to a full-blown inquiry
into the various ways stories and poems are put together.
The children may wish to collect and categorize
favorite stories and poems they have read in the past:
repetitive, cumulative, interlocking, familiar cultural sequences,
problem-centered, rhythm-rhyme scheme.
All of this activity should have the zestful spirit
of scientific inquiry.
The children's satisfaction will come
from really figuring out
how something in their world works.

If you are teaching older boys and girls
who have never had experiences
with this approach to word-unlocking,
you may wish to get hold of a set of *Instant Readers.*[11]
These Bill Martin books are written
around the basic literary structures
and the books are discussed from this point of view
in the Teachers Guide.
Because the books are short and the structures are exaggerated,
the children can analyze them more easily
than they can longer stories.
You can also use the earlier *Sounds of Language* readers
with older boys and girls
if you reassure them
that you are doing grown-up things with the books.
Once you get into analyzing the author's plan
for putting his story together,
the children will respect the use of the younger books.

[11] Holt, Rinehart and Winston Inc.

And don't forget to browse through
the *Sounds of Language* books provided
for your particular class.
In even the seventh and eighth grade anthologies
you will find numerous short selections
that lend themselves to obvious literary analysis.

You may have to remind yourself
that these books do not have to be read
page-by-page from cover to cover
as most other readers do.
You can pick and choose from anywhere in the book,
depending on the interests and purposes
of the children and yourself.
Neither do the selections have to be exploited
in a single lesson and then left as "finished."
You can return to favorite selections
dozens of times throughout the year
for different purposes.

> *Boys and girls, do you remember*
> *the story "Ming and Ling"*[12]
> *that we enjoyed so much?*
> *Let's take another look at it. This time . . .*

Who knows how many useful excursions
children can conduct
through a story or poem that has been deposited
in their linguistic storehouses.
This is the reason for depositing the literature—
to make it available for a lifetime
of analysis and pleasure.

[12] *Sounds Freedomring*

Some of the best opportunities
for analyzing literary structure will come
when the children are borrowing the author's pattern
and hanging their thoughts and vocabulary on it.

*Boys and girls, let's take a look
at this rather simple story:*

*"I am not as big as a goat.
A goat is bigger than I am.*

*I am not as big as a horse.
A horse is bigger than I am.*

*I am not as big as an elephant.
An elephant is bigger than I am.*

*I am not as big as a whale.
A whale is bigger than I am.*

*I am not as big as a dinosaur.
A dinosaur is the biggest thing I know."*

—from "What Is Big?" *Sounds of Numbers*

*If you were to borrow
the author's exact pattern
and make your own story out of it,
what would be important to remember?
Do you think you can make
even a simple pattern like this
interesting to fourth graders?*

The children will probably verbalize
that the author has a plan for repeating.
They will probably notice that the describing word *big*
is central to the language pattern.
They may comment on his way for breaking the pattern
to bring the story to a close.
They may comment that the creatures
keep growing larger.
Fourth graders have been known
to come up with innovations
on even simple structures
that give them pleasure.

I am not as bony as my sister.
My sister is bonier than I am.

I am not as bony as a fish.
A fish is bonier than I am.

I am not as bony as spareribs.
Spareribs are bonier than I am.

I am not as bony as a skeleton.
A skeleton is the boniest thing I know.

—from a fourth grader, Corbett School, Tucson, Arizona

A sixth grader chooses the pattern from "A Turkey Speaks"
in *Sounds of a Distant Drum* for his innovation.

Taco Speaks

I have never understood
why anyone would
roast the shell
buy the meat
chip the pickles
chop the lettuce
when they could
sit back
and call . . . .

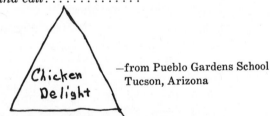

—from Pueblo Gardens School
Tucson, Arizona

Gradually you can help the children generalize
that when they are reading on their own
it is a good idea to be curious
about how the author put his story together
and that once they get the *aha!* feeling,
meaning that they have caught on to his plan,
they will be partly prepared for the vocabulary
they will encounter,
and that their structural insight
is both a writing and a reading skill.

6 FIGURING OUT HOW SENTENCES WORK

In the same sense
that a story has a shape
and a poem has a shape,
so does a sentence have a shape.
A speaker pauses, intones, gestures
to show how the words group together
and thereby reveal his meanings.
A writer uses punctuation
to help the reader see
how the words group together.

The concept of *shapes of sentences*
is somewhat implied
in our earlier discussion of *chunks of meaning*.
In speaking and writing,
words do not simply follow one another
in unrelated separateness.
They cluster together to form a chunk of meaning
and these chunks of meaning
are basic to the shape of a sentence.
Not only that.
These chunks of meaning within a sentence
do not simply follow one another in random style.
They form a pattern as they fall next to one another
and recognizing the pattern is helpful in decoding.
One additional facet in the shaping of a sentence
is the fact that there is a definite order
in which many individual words fall in English sentences.
A chunk of meaning about a pretty girl
will not reverse this culturally established order
and call her a *girl pretty*.

Let's take a closer look
at these three characteristics
that influence the shapes of sentences
and see what the implications are
for developing reading skills
that are not provided for in most reading programs.

A) Sentences Work in Chunks of Meaning

One useful way to help children understand
that chunks of meaning
are basic to the shape of a sentence,
is to read aloud a sentence from a familiar story
and ask the children to keep their books closed
and raise their hands each time
they hear a chunk of meaning:

So the little squeegy bug
followed Creepy the Caterpillar
to his home under the cattail leaf,
and soon was safe and warm,
away from the storm,
and he slept soundly
until morning.

—from "Little Squeegy Bug," *Sounds After Dark*

Remind the children that different people may hear
different chunks of meaning
so they will not be worried about right and wrong answers
when they enter into a later discussion
of where the various chunks begin and end.

At no time should a child feel embarrassed
over his selection of a chunk of meaning.
Even if he errs,
he will self-correct (the hallmark of an educated person)
when he becomes comfortable with this concept.
And by the way, if you should find yourself
selecting different chunks of meaning
from the ones we have indicated
in the sentence from "The Little Squeegy Bug,"
don't become alarmed.
Frequently more than one choice is possible.
The test is: *Does the selection of a particular chunk of meaning
have integrity in and of itself,
and does it leave a complete chunk on either side of it?*

Another useful way to help children latch on
to the chunks-of-meaning concept
is to compare the line-by-line text of a story
which is arranged in chunks of meaning
in a *Sounds of Language* reader
with a chapter in their social studies book or other textbook
where traditional paragraphing style is used
to shape sentences to rigid right-left hand margins
regardless of chunks of meaning.
On the opposite page is a pictorial comparison
of language in paragraph form
with language in chunks of meaning.
Which more readily invites your reading interest?
Since a chunk of meaning is a unit of sense,
the children may profit from discussing
whether or not breaking the sentences into units of sense
makes for more reader ease and understanding.
Accept any observations the children care to make.
Some children may be so accustomed
to the rigid right-left hand margins
that they actually find this newer page design more difficult at first.
Whatever their reactions,
this kind of comparing and free discussion
will further their understanding of the fact
that sentences work in chunks of meaning.

BLIZZARD HITS WESTERN STATES

AIR FORCE'S "OPERATION FEEDLIFT" BALKED BY CONTINUING BLIZZARD

CHICAGO, Jan. 20—One of the worst storms in memory hit Montana, eastern Washington, Utah, Nevada, Wyoming, Colorado and the Dakotas today in the form of blizzards, floods and bitter Arctic cold.

Some areas were buried under as much as 80 inches of snow, which forced the closing of schools and blocked highways. Freezing winds blew roofs off buildings, smashed windows and ripped down power and telephone lines. Brief gusts of the blizzard winds reached speeds as high as 95 miles an hour in parts of Montana and the Dakotas.

CHICAGO, Jan. 20—
One of the worst storms in memory
hit Montana,
eastern Washington,
Utah,
Nevada,
Wyoming,
Colorado
and the Dakotas today
in the form of blizzards,
floods
and bitter Arctic cold.

Some areas were buried
under as much as
80 inches of snow,
which forced
the closing of schools
and blocked highways.
Freezing winds
blew roofs off buildings,
smashed windows
and ripped down
power and telephone lines.
Brief gusts of the blizzard winds
reached speeds
as high as
95 miles an hour
in parts of Montana
and the Dakotas.

—from *Sounds of a Distant Drum*

At some point in your figuring out how sentences work,
you will want to invite the children
to take a paragraph from a story or article
that is printed with the traditional right-hand margin
and break the sentences into chunks of meaning.
The markings may vary from child to child
but no marking should violate a unit of sense.
When variations do occur,
be sure to discuss the children's reasoning
back of their choices
to determine whether or not
a child is sensing the meaning
back of the clustering of words he has selected.

Somewhere during your discussion of ways
for breaking the rigid right-hand material
into chunks of meaning,
you will want to help the children verbalize the fact
that once they are able to break unbroken sentences
into chunks of meaning,
they are developing a skill
that will stand them in good stead
in their independent reading.
Gradually they will build the habit
of seeing chunks of meaning
whether or not the text has been printed that way.
This is germane to dealing
with the meaning encased in print.

You may wish to consider punctuation
while you are discussing chunks of meaning.
As a matter of fact,
this may be the first time
some of your children see the actual sense to punctuation.
They may have seen commas and periods
and all the rest
primarily as items to get right or wrong
as they fill in blanks in workbooks.
Now with this new look at the ways sentences work,
they may enjoy discussing
how punctuation came to be in the first place.

When man invented the code
that we call written language,
he immediately found the need
for additional inventions besides the letters
to make writing work.
He therefore invented periods and commas
and other signals
to help the reader hear
what the code was saying.
Won't it be interesting
if the children decide
that printing sentences
in chunks of meaning
can make
certain punctuation
unnecessary!

SOX SONG
RED SOX
BLUE SOX
WHITE SOX
GREEN SOX
BROWN SOX
BLACK SOX
COLORS·IN·BETWEEN SOX

—from *Sounds After Dark*

The pickety fence

The pickety fence
Give it a lick it's
The pickety fence
Give it a lick it's
A clickety fence
Give it a lick it's
A lickety fence
Give it a lick
Give it a lick
Give it a lick
With a rickety stick
Pickety
Pickety
Pickety
Pick

—by David McCord,
from *Sounds of a Young Hunter*

B) Sentences Work Because of WORD ORDER

One other characteristic of English sentences,
is the *order* in which individual words
are placed next to one another.
A three-year-old knows this.
He will say:

> *Me hit you.*

It is true he is using
the incorrect form of the pronoun,
but he will not ruin the basic shape
of the sentence and say:

> *Hit me you.*

He will not rearrange the usual word-order
and put the verb in front of the subject pronoun.
He will say

> *big boy*

He will not say

> *boy big*

He will not deny the fact
that in the English language
the adjective usually comes in front of the noun.
As a school child,
if he is helped to experiment with sentences
and to verbalize his intuitive knowledge
about word-order in English sentences,
he will partially unlock words
because of where they fall
and what function they perform in the sentence.
That child coming to this sentence, for example,

I found six spotted puppies.

will not sit and endlessly spit and sputter
over the *sp* sound in *spotted*
and then give up in despair if he can't sound out the word.

He will first of all recognize
that *spotted* is a describing word,
falling as it does, in front of *puppies*.
With this dependable structural clue,
he finds it useful to know that the word begins
with the *sp* sounds.
Knowing that the word describes *puppies*
narrows the range, as it were,
to the short array of culturally anticipated words
such as:

> *little puppies*
> *white puppies*
> *black puppies*
> *tiny puppies*
> *collie puppies*
> *friendly puppies*
> *hungry puppies*
> *spotted puppies*

Instead of being confronted with the whole wide world
of words at random
he now is seeking only an *sp* word that can appropriately
describe *puppies*,

> *spotted puppies.*

What a difference in psychological posture!
What a cultural reliability
that supports a child's best efforts!

In a different context,
a writer sometimes distorts natural *word order*
for emphasis on rhythm or dramatic effect
as Walter de la Mare does in this amazing sentence:

> All but blind
> In his chambered hole
> Gropes for worms
> The four-clawed Mole.

> —from "All But Blind," *Sounds of Mystery*

C) Sentences Work in Sequence Patterns

Another characteristic of English sentences
is the way in which
the various chunks of meaning
are connected with one another.
Interestingly enough,
these clusters of words
pattern in much the same way
that the episodes in a story pattern.

1) Repetitive Sequence

Over in the meadow
in the sand
in the sun
Lived an old mother turtle and her little turtle one.

—from "Over in the Meadow," *Sounds of a Powwow*

Repetition of chunks of meaning
is central to the shape
of this sentence.
Leave out *in the sand* and *in the sun*
and the basic design of the sentence
has been altered.
Once the basic designs for arranging sentences
have been deposited in the children's linguistic storehouses,
they own them for a lifetime of transforming
in their speaking and reading and writing.

2) Cumulative Sequence

Sometimes the chunks of meaning in a sentence
just keep adding on to one another
to give the sentence its shape.

Then, each monkey pulled off his cap . . .

and all the yellow caps . . .

and all the blue caps . . .

and all the red caps . . .

and all the polkadot caps . . .

came flying $d o_{w_{n}}$ $o_{u} t$ of the tree.

—from "Caps for Sale," *Sounds of a Powwow*

Young children are great at writing cumulative sentences
once they discover the power in the little word *and*.
You've seen these sentences:

> *I went home from school*
> *and then I . . .*
> *and then I . . .*
> *and then I . . .*
> *and then I . . .*

Instead of criticizing the children
in our well-intentioned effort
to get them to write more interesting sentences,
we should praise them for their discovery.

Julie, that's just about the longest sentence
I ever saw.
Did you know that all of your life
you'll be seeing and hearing sentences that are put
together that way? Let's take a look at your long sentence
and see if we can figure out how it goes together.
How did it get to be so long?

Accept any homely observations
the children care to make.

Well, I just kept saying
"and then, and then, and then . . ."

is a beginning verbalization
of the shape of a cumulative sentence.

If the children made observations
about the cumulative sequencing
from episode to episode in "The House that Jack Built,"
they may enjoy going back to the story now:

This is the COCK that crowed in the morn,

That waked the priest all shaven and shorn,

That married the man all tattered and torn,

That kissed the maiden all forlorn,

That milked the cow

with the crumpled horn,

That tossed the dog, that worried the cat,

That killed the rat, That ate the malt,

That lay in the house that Jack built.

—from *Sounds Around the Clock*

Imagine what fun it will be to discover
that each new episode is actually a cumulative sentence.

In your discussion of the various ways
chunks of meaning are laid next to one another
in a sentence,
don't press for exact terminology.
Older boys and girls may enjoy some terminology
after they have explored the shapes of sentences (and stories)
but the most important part of the explorations
is their homely verbalizing of their self-selected observations
about the ways in which sentences work.

3) Interlocking Sequence

> Down by the river,
> Down by the river,
> Down by the river so green,
> Down by the river where daffodils grow,
> Down by the river where breezes blow,
> Down by the river where butterflies flit,
> That's where firefly lamps are lit.
>
> —from *Sounds I Remember*

Sometimes the chunks of meaning in sentences
do not simply repeat or add on.
They interlock with one another
(as the chunks do in the sample sentence here)
in ways that create the sentence form and meaning.
For the most part,
an interlocked sentence does not reveal its full meaning
until the last segment in the chain of interlocking.

Consider, for example,
how incomplete the meaning of the following sentence is
until the last segment hinges in:

To the Sun
Who has shone
  All day,
To the Moon
Who has gone
  Away,
To the milk-white,
Lily-white Star
A fond goodnight
Wherever you are.

—"Last Song," by James Guthrie,
Sounds of a Distant Drum

Did you notice the repetitive sequence of this sentence?
And also that the sentence maintains a simultaneous
repetitive and interlocking sequence.
Interestingly enough,
as you will observe in the two sample sentences given here,
the chunks of meaning in one
can be reordered (re-arranged) without destroying the meaning,
while in the other
the various chunks of meaning cannot be rearranged
without destroying both the shape and meaning of the sentence.
It is as if a cyclone came along
and stripped the sentence of its sense.
Of all the sentence patterns,
the interlocking sequence is perhaps the one
that best helps children understand
that sentences are not simply long strings of isolated words
hung together with a capital letter and a period.

Sentences, like stories,
are shapes within a shape.
They are chunks of meaning
which are laid next to one another
according to a design.
Recognizing the design
helps to unlock the meaning.

4) Chronological Sequence

Chronological sentences are probably the easiest
to figure out
in terms of recognizing their basic shape.
Everything moves ahead so orderly:

First, the

outside surface of your upper teeth; second, the

The same three areas of the lower teeth need careful cleaning: 1) outside, 2) inside, 3) biting edge.

inside surface of these teeth; third,

the grinding surfaces of the upper teeth.

—from "How to Brush Your Teeth," *Sounds of a Young Hunter*

Here's another sample:

Then he reached up

to make sure that they were straight—

first his own striped cap,

then the four yellow caps,

then the four blue caps,

then the four red caps,

then on the very top the four polkadot caps.

—from "Caps for Sale," *Sounds of a Powwow*

And still another which is nonetheless chronological
because the time sequence is less obvious.

So she (the Grandmarina)
took it (the Magic Fishbone)
from the hand of Princess Alicia
and waved her magic fan over it,
and it instantly flew
down the throat
of the dreadful little
snapping pug dog next door
and nearly choked him,
and that was good!

—from "The Magic Fishbone," *Sounds Jubilee*

Once children sense that a sentence is moving forward
in chronological sequence,
they join right in with the author (anticipate)
in planning how the chunks of meaning will be arranged.

This kind of feeling that it is possible
to work one's way through a complicated looking sentence
because of recognizing its structure,
develops into a highly useful work-unlocking skill.

5) Rhyme-Rhythm Sequence

You can take a tub with a rub and a scrub

in a two-foot tank of TIN,

You can stand and look at the whirling brook

and think about jumping IN;

You can chatter and shake in the cold black lake,

but the kind of bath for ME,

Is to take a dip from the side of a ship,

in the trough of the rolling SEA.

—from "The Kind of a Bath for Me,"
Sounds of the Storyteller

This sentence moves forward
with a rhyme-rhythm sequence that helps give it its shape.
Children will readily recognize
that the intrigue and charm of the sentence
stem equally from the rhyme—
both internal and terminal— and from the rhythm.

In the following example, however,
it is the anticipation of rhyme, not rhythm,
that focuses the sentence sequence
and the unlocking of the word *precisely*.

. . . putting it my way, but nicely,

You are precisely my cup of tea!

—from "Getting to Know You," *Sounds of the Storyteller*

Here again, it's rhythm, not rhyme, that shapes a sentence:

N ow, pray, where are you going?"
                    said Meet-on-the-Road.
  "To school, sir, to school, sir,"
                    said Child-as-it-Stood.

—from "Meet on the Road," *Sounds After Dark*

Here is another sentence
so rhythmically shaped
that it stands alone like a poem:

O NCE IN THE GOLDEN TIME
      when an Irish king sat in every province
      and plenty covered the land,
    there lived in Connaught
    a grand old king with one daughter.

—from "The Princess and the Vagabond,"
Sounds of a Distant Drum

By clapping the rhythm of these sentences
and others that appeal,
children can develop sensitivity
to the rhythm of language,
a skill absolutely essential to anyone
who is to make a go of writing and reading.
You can, for example, invite someone to clap out a page of print
that all of the class has read frequently
to see if the selection can be recognized
solely by the linguistic rhythm.
At the same time
the children will be developing syllabication skills
in a far more functional setting
than looking a word up in a dictionary
for its stressed and unstressed patterns.

By clapping (and dancing) the rhythm of a sentence:

> I hoe and I plow
> I plow and I hoe
> And the wind drives over the main.
>
> I mow and I plant
> I plant and I mow
> While the sun burns hot on the plain.
>
> —from "Farmer" by Liberty Hyde Bailey,
> *Sounds After Dark*

the children will be getting the language
into their muscles as well as their minds,
a childhood naturality that makes language learning
pleasant and easy
until the pedants take over and deny children the use
of their basic language learning equipment.

Obviously there are other basic shapes to sentences
than the ones suggested in this essay,
but our purpose in this discussion is simply to alert you
that the clusters of words within a sentence
do fall together in various patterns
and that recognition of the pattern
is an aid in word-unlocking.
You may wish to jot down a few sentences from a favorite story
and see what observations you can make
about the patterns into which
the clusters of words fall.
First divide the sentences into their chunks of meaning
as we have done on these pages.
Then you are on your own.
Far more important than labeling the various shapes
is the recognition that sentences are not strings of words
which happen to fall together.

7 INNOVATING ON SENTENCE PATTERNS

By now you know
that when you read aloud to children
you are depositing various sentence patterns
in the children's linguistic storehouses
for a lifetime of use.
You probably are also aware
that when the children chime in on the reading,
especially in alive and dramatic ways
that include bodily movement,
they are themselves claiming and depositing these patterns.
One further activity
to help make these basic sentence structures
easily available to children for word-unlocking
in their reading and for writing and speaking,
is to invite them into systematic
and at the same time creative and lively experimenting
with the various patterns.
Here are four sentence manipulations
which have proved especially useful
for this kind of experimentation.

A) Transforming Sentences

Transforming a sentence
is the act of using the exact structure of a sentence
as the basis for creating a semantically new sentence
through either word-by-word substitution
or substitution of whole clusters of words.

I never saw a purple cow.
—from Sounds of Numbers

Your first step in helping children transform this sentence,
after all of you have enjoyed reading the whole poem
from which it came,
is to copy the model sentence on the chalkboard,
leaving space between each word.
Then your conversation goes something like this:

> *Children, I'm going to draw a line*
> *to the word* cow.
> *Now, supposing we didn't want*
> *to use the word* cow.
> *What other words could we use*
> *instead of* cow?

Suggestions will begin to flow.

I never saw a purple cow.

    horse
    pig
    rabbit

Children, all of our naming words are animals.
Supposing we wanted another kind of naming word—
one that would make a spooky sentence.

I never saw a purple cow.

    horse
    pig
    rabbit
    spook
    vampire

Now, children, supposing we didn't want
to use the word purple?
Who else has a describing word?

Again the suggestions will flow.

I   never   saw   a   **purple**   **cow.**

brown	horse
pink	pig
hungry	rabbit
wailing	spook
	vampire

And so it goes until the children have suggested
vocabulary substitutions for all of the words.
You may wish to enter the game,
especially if the children are not having fun
with the substitutions they suggest.

Children, does anyone in this class
like silly sentences?
Well, I'm going to give you a new action word
that will really make a silly sentence.

I   never   **saw**   a   purple   cow.

kissed
loved
hugged
milked
married

Now the lid is off and the children's merriment
knows no bounds as they contemplate kissing purple vampires
and marrying pink spooks.
You may wish to invite the children

to go back to their tables
to write sentences of their choice.
At some point you may wish
to begin gentle conversation
about the word order in the sentence.

> *Isn't it interesting, children,*
> *that we don't say:*
>
> **I never saw a cow purple.**
>
> *I wonder why not.*

The children will probably suggest
that it just doesn't sound good—
meaning that their ears have already picked up
the usual word order in English sentences.
Gradually these kinds of conversations
help children add information
to their growing notions about how sentences work.
The *Sounds of Language* readers abound
in useful sentence patterns for the children to transform.
We have annotated a few of these sentences
to get you and the children started.
No attempt has been made to annotate every sentence
that lend itself to this kind of language analysis.
The peak value of the activity will come
when you and the children learn to go over a story
after enjoying it in its wholeness,
perusing it for *model sentences* rich in analysis potential.
It is your and the children's own selection
and manipulation of *model sentences*
that firmly connects the language learnings
with a child's personal use of language.
This is a qualitatively different learning experience
from that of filling in little blanks
in typical language workbooks.

Imagine what fun you and the children will have
when you select an intriguing sentence like this one
from E. B. White's *Charlotte's Web*
as a model to transform:

Soon the children will be far-ranging in their choices
of serious and silly sentences offered by the framework:

They   hated   the   incessant   dripping   of   the   rain

The witch dreamed of a heady ride   on her broomstick

The motor made a suspicious wheezing   during the night

From time to time, you yourself will want
to suggest a vocabulary substitution
such as *skeleton, ghost, ferocious, monotonous,*
knowing that one strong, colorful word
will result in a flurry of additional substitutions.
When children become deeply involved
in transforming activities,
there's never time for each of them to read aloud
all of their self-selected sentences.

along **his** **itchy** **back.**

under	her	itchy	hayrack
over	their	rough	bridge
along	the	rusty	terrain
in	that	tired	drainpipe
on	our	trusty	fence
at		creaking	brow
above		sagging	bed
		saggy	ear

through   the   sagging   roof.

with her irritable cat.

of our scary escape.

This offers an opportunity for them to write sentences
that eventually they can read to one another.
You can also suggest to the children
that they keep in their notebooks
a list of model sentences that especially appeal to them
for later transforming in their personal writing.
Awarenesses of this kind
are a sound linguistic base for both reading and writing.

B) Expanding Sentences

Expanding sentences is another technique
for helping children become aware
of the shape of sentences
and for helping them develop this awareness
into reading and writing and speaking skills.
This sentence manipulation is exactly
what the term *expanding* connotes.
Any simple sentence can be expanded
by adding phrases, clauses or describing words.

*Children, let's take a sentence
from our old jingle, "Susie Moriar."*

This   is   the   story   of   Susie   Moriar.

*Let's see if we can think of some describing words
to put in front of* Susie.

This   is   the   story   of   Susie   Moriar.
                                    funny
                                    kind
                                    nice

*Now let's think of some describing words
to put in front of* story.

This   is   the   story   of   Susie   Moriar.
                    rhyming   funny
                    silly   kind
                    impossible   nice

Now who would like to try reading a sentence
using any of the words on the board?
Have you noticed, boys and girls,
how our sentence is getting longer and longer?
There is one other way we can expand this sentence
and make it even longer.
We can add a whole collection of words
that belong together.

This   is   the͏̂   story   of͏̂   Susie   Moriar͏̂.

rhyming	funny	who lost her teeth
silly	kind	who likes to bake cakes
impossible	nice	who stands on her head

It's easy to see
that in writing the following sentence,
Anthony could have started with the simple statement:

> The   king   was   old.

and then expanded it:

The King was so old
he could not dance the
twist so he said to
one of his girls to hold
him and do the twist
in slow motion.

—1st Grade, J. J. Ingalls School
Kansas City, Kansas

Older boys and girls search their linguistic storehouses
for single words and clusters of words
to make their sentence expanding worthwhile:

two
friendly
crowd of
adventurous
unsuspecting

a warning
a greeting
in glee
wildly
, "Hello, friend!"

The girls shouted and ran over

All of a sudden
Without a warning
Their hopes high,
Hoping for the best,
When they arrived,
After the parade was over,

directly
breathlessly
excitedly
their fastest
as fast as they could
head over heels

An expanded sentence can be more dramatic,
"paint more pictures,"
or produce a more interesting array of sounds,
but it is not necessarily a better sentence.
In the process of expanding sentences, however,
children become keenly aware of the placement and function
of phrases and clauses and individual words
within a sentence.
And as they read their expanded sentences aloud,
they overtly are making judgments
about the kinds of sentences they do and do not like,
thus taking another step in the development of
and appreciation for a personal style
in writing and speaking.
It is this aware development
of a personal style
that helps children appreciate the fact
that authors of stories and poems
also have preferred styles.

```
              ┌ new
              │ old
              │ big
              │ open
              │ dilapidated
              │ comfortable
              │ air-conditioned
              └ well-lighted

  to    Hippy Hippo's    cage ↑ .
                         ┌ nearby
                         │ in the arena
                         │ beyond the bridge
                         └ under the tree
```

—from "Hippy Hippo," *Sounds of Mystery*

A child with this kind of awareness
can browse through the first few pages
of a book he has selected from the library shelf
and make beginning judgments about the kinds of words
he will be unlocking simply by conning the author's sentence style.
If the sentences are involved
and packed with adjectives and adverbs,
this child will be sending signals to his linguistic storehouse,
as it were,
to trigger stored patterns to help with the reading ahead.

C) Transforming and Expanding Sentences

As children gain skill in sentence manipulations,
they will undoubtedly want to combine
two or more of the methods suggested here.
For example, colorful sentence possibilities emerge
when a model sentence is both transformed and expanded.
Consider the wide range of sentences
that is inherent in this diagram:

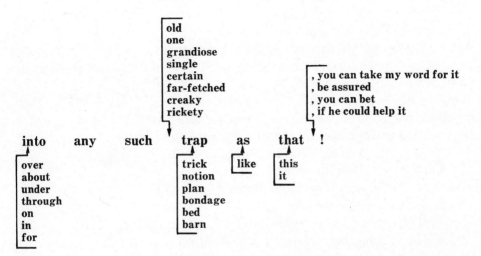

old
one
grandiose
single
certain
far-fetched
creaky
rickety

, you can take my word for it
, be assured
, you can bet
, if he could help it

into   any   such   trap   as   that !

over
about
under
through
on
in
for

trick
notion
plan
bondage
bed
barn

like

this
it

—from "How Boots Befooled the King," *Sounds of Mystery*

D) Reducing Sentences

Another sentence manipulation
that is highly useful in helping children
figure out how sentences work
is reducing sentences.
When a person reduces a sentence,
he eliminates all unnecessary words, phrases and clauses.
The danger in reducing a sentence is that one is apt
to alter or destroy the sentence meaning
or to tamper with the author's style of writing.
As you and the children go through your *Sounds of Language* readers
in search of sentences to reduce,
you may have the same difficulty we had
when we searched for sentences to annotate for you.
The sentences are generally too well written for reducing.
However, in terms of children's learning,
the search is what is important.
As they consider which words or phrases or clauses
can or can't be eliminated,
they will be experimenting with the shapes of sentences
and will be storing their learnings for later use.
Now let's reduce a few sentences and analyze the results.

A bird also has another way to help keep himself warm in winter.

By seeing to it that the birds near your home have plenty to eat,
you can help "keep their furnaces roaring" and
their bodies warm in winter.

The bird's outer feathers
are staggered like shingles on a roof
to keep out the rain and snow.

—from "How Birds Keep Warm in Winter," *Sounds of Mystery*

In the first sentence, the reducing sharpened the sentence.
The eliminated words are truly unnecessary.

In the second sentence,
the meaning is definitely altered by the deletions.
In the third sentence,
the question is not so much whether meaning has been altered
but whether the author's style has been tampered with.
As the children read Bernard Martin's article,
they will discover that here is an author
who paints pictures in the sentences he writes.
By eliminating such a vivid picture as
(feathers) *staggered like shingles on a roof,*
the sentence is rendered unimaginative,
albeit the sentence still makes its point
that the bird's feathers keep out the rain and snow.
One useful question to ask the children
after they have reduced an author's sentence is:

> *What do you think Bernard Martin*
> *would think about his sentence now?*

If they are referring to the third sentence above,
some children will probably conclude:

> *Well, he probably wouldn't like it very much.*

Then it can be profitable to look at other sentences
that suffer from being reduced.
The children may wish to turn
to a discussion of their own preferred sentence styles:

> *Jerry, would you say that you like best*
> *to write reduced or expanded sentences?*

More than one Jerry has been known to respond:

> *Well, I really like to write reduced sentences*
> *but you're always trying to get me*
> *to write expanded sentences.*

There are no right or wrong answers to these kinds
of linguistic inquiries.
Hopefully, the children will become versatile enough
to write and read many sentence styles.

Of one thing we are certain
from our observations in research classrooms
around the country:
children who have opportunities
to experiment with the shapes of sentences
will never again view reading as a matter
of sounding out isolated words.
They will not easily bog down or stop dead in their tracks
when they come to unknown words
because they will feel the strength of the language know-how
deposited in their linguistic storehouses
both in the form of literary and linguistic patterns
and in the form of worthwhile generalizations
about how language works
which they formulate in experimentation and discussion.

E)   Rearranging Sentences

As we have already discussed,
ours is a word-order language.
The function of a word is highly dependent
on its position in the sentence.

> *I never saw a purple cow.*

A person who has listened to English sentences
all of his life, be he seven or seventy,
will hunch that the word *purple*
describes the word *cow,*
falling as it does directly in front of *cow.*
To change the word *the*
from first to second position in this sentence

> *The day is gone.*

destroys the meaning of the sentence
because the structure has been destroyed.
On the other hand,
the structure of some sentences
is not inflexible.

Jan came crying with her broken doll in hand.

can be significantly rearranged within the limitations
of our language system without a loss of meaning:

With her broken doll in hand, Jan came crying.
Jan came, with her broken doll in hand, crying.
Crying, with her broken doll in hand, came Jan.

Let's consider the sentence patterned on internal rhyme
which we enjoyed earlier in this discussion:

1) You can take a tub

2) with a rub

3) and a scrub

4) in a two-foot tank of tin.

This sentence can be easily rearranged 2–3–1–4
without destroying the structure or meaning.
You probably see other possibilities for rearranging,
while retaining the structure and meaning.
Consider the following sentence in the same light.
You readily can see multiple possibilities
for rearranging this sentence:

A truck came bumping
along the shore road,
its headlights shining
through the weeds.

—from "The Web of Winter," *Sounds of Mystery*

When you work with sentences this way on the chalkboard,
be sure to invite the children to make judgments
as to which arrangement they prefer.
This is germane to developing a personal style in writing,
for it is only by putting words together
in ways that are consistent with personality
that a person develops a *style* of writing.

Rearranging sentences is one of the many structural activities
that mark *Sounds of Language* as a comprehensive linguistic program.
Unlike some linguistic programs
that focus primarily on the shape of words,
Sounds of Language accepts realistically the fact
that the sentence is the basic unit of meaning in our language
and that an understanding of sentence structure
is basic to intaking sentence meaning.

Rearranging sentences best begins
with a recognition of the clusters of words
which are arranged in a particular way
to create the basic shape of the sentence.
Once a sentence has been divided into chunks of meaning,
a useful question is:

> *Children, do you see any clusters of words in this sentence*
> *which could be moved around?*

This awareness of movable parts in a sentence
helps children in reading long and difficult sentences.
Not only do they learn to read through it one chunk at a time,
but they also learn,
if a sentence has a difficult beginning,
to start reading the sentence at an easier point
and later pick up the more difficult chunks
when they have some sentence context to help them.
In unlocking this sentence, for example,
a child who has gained skill in rearranging sentences
will not bog down on the introductory chunk of meaning
if the words are unfamiliar to him.

> Pressing his lithe body
>
> against the plastered wall,
>
> he listened
>
> and heard Nag and Nagaina
>
> whispering together
>
> outside in the moonlight.

—"Rikki Tikki Tavi," *Sounds of Mystery*

Rather, he will skip down to the third chunk,
he listened,
which offers a more direct entry into the sentence.
Certain children have intuitively done this
as the natural way for making a go of a book,
until narrow reading instruction cuts them off
from this sensible, linguistically sound way
for handling complex print,
and instead teaches them to stop dead in their tracks
while they try to sound out each word
in that complicated first chunk of meaning.

Throughout *Sounds of Language* you will find
type arranged in unique and intriguing patterns—
part of our scheme to invite children
to use chunks of meaning to unlock
the linguistic puzzle.

I LOVE YOU, BIG WORLD. I wish I could call you. And tell you a secret: That I love you, World...

by *Paul Wollner*

AGE 7

UNITED STATES

—from *Sounds of a Powwow*

8 FIGURING OUT HOW WORDS WORK

In basal reading programs and phonics programs
children spend their waking hours
considering the various ways in which words work.
In fact, in most of these programs
the word seems to be the only unit of language
worth studying.
Children learn about beginnings of words
and ends of words and middles of words.
They learn about special endings such as inflected endings.
They learn how the various letters behave in words.
And all of this they learn (or try to learn)
in line with prescriptive lesson plans
laid out in the teacher's guide.
When it is beginning consonant season,
heaven help the child who is good at looking at ends of words.
In some programs, children have to wait to beginning second grade
to even know that words have middles,
because that is when the teacher's guide
presents medial vowels.
Moreover, the methods used in teaching about words
are largely prescriptive.
Children are not invited to experiment with words
and come up with their own generalizations.
They are asked to memorize other people's generalizations
about what happens when two vowels go walking,
even though we all know that the first one does the talking
only when it feels in the mood.

You may or may not be using one of these programs
in your classroom.
Whether you do or not,
you and your children still need
the kind of spontaneous word analysis time
that is made possible with the *Sounds of Language* program.

In the same way that the children figure out
how stories and poems and sentences work
by experimenting with structures and verbalizing their discoveries,
children need to use their self-selected ways
for figuring out how words work.

Sometimes your open-ended questioning after reading a story or poem
will trigger discussions
which help children figure out how words pattern.
Supposing you have read:

One Misty, Moisty Morning

When cloudy was the weather,

I chanced to meet an old man

Clothed all in leather.

He began to compliment

And I began to grin:

"How do you do?"

And "How do you do?"

And "How do you do?" again.

—from *Sounds of Numbers*

After you and the children have thoroughly enjoyed the poem
through oral and various arrangements of choral reading
and after the children are using books
so their eyes are seeing the same patterns that their ears are hearing,
you might ask:

> *Children, what do you see interesting
> about those two words* misty *and* moisty?

Accept any observations the children care to make.

If Henry tells you that they both **Misty, Moisty**
have *y* at the end,
don't become ill at ease
if you are only studying beginning consonants
in your other reading program.
Some children are better at observing the ends of words
than they are at observing the beginnings of words
when they first start looking at print.
If these children learn
that nice boys don't look at the ends of words
simply because a prescriptive phonics program
is insisting on beginning sounds,
they begin to feel that there is something wrong
about them and reading
and they learn not to focus on the patterns of words
and certainly not to report their observations
if they do take a look.
How much better to praise Henry
for his accurate observation.

> *Henry, you're so great*
> *at looking at the ends of words.*
> *Perhaps you can find something else interesting*
> *about the way* misty *and* moisty *end.*

By now Henry is with you full force.
And on the heels of his success
in looking at the ends of words,
he can probably also be invited
to take a look at the beginnings of the two words.
By now some child will probably report to you,

> *Look.* **Moisty** *is bigger in the middle.*

Now the children have come face-to-face
with an interesting generalization about the ways words work.
They have beginnings and endings and middles.

inggallopinggallopinggallopinggallopinggallopinggc
ggallopinggallopinggallopinggallopinggallopinggall
gallopinggallopinggallopinggallopinggallopinggallop

The generalization has meaning
because in the first place,
they were scrutinizing the printed form
of two words that entered their linguistic storehouses
through the heat and drama of read-aloud.
They are not just cold words on a workbook page.
They are words the children truly own.
The generalization also has meaning
because the children were able to sneak up on it,
as it were,
knowing it intuitively from their experiences
with oral language
and gradually verbalizing this facet
of the shape of words they are seeing in print.

One useful question
for getting this kind of discussion going is simply:

*Children, what do you see interesting
about the words on this page?*

As the children report observations
about how letters fall next to one another in words
you will have an interesting diagnostic
of who the individual children are as word-unlockers.
The child who reports seeing three words
that "all have two t's in the middle"
is telling you that he sees letter patterns in words.
The child who reports a word
"that looks just like a fish,"
may be telling you that he is one of those children
who goes into reading by seeing pictures in words
rather than spelling patterns.
How exciting!

—from a word design from *Sounds of a Distant Drum*

ggallopinggallopinggallopinggallopinggallopinggall
gallopinggallopinggallopinggallopinggallopinggallop
llopinggallopinggallopinggallopinggallopinggallopir

One productive activity
in helping primary children figure out how words work
(as well as how sentences work),
is to invite them to collect word cards
that they especially want.
This is markedly different from handing out
the same word cards to all children
with the requirement that they learn the word
as part of their basal reading program.
In this latter approach, it is the teacher who is reaching out,
trying to capture the child
and get him to learn the word selected by the teacher's guide.
When children ask for word cards of their own choosing,
they are the ones doing the reaching-out
and consequently the motivation comes from within themselves
rather than from the pressures of the outside world.
Children the nation over
demonstrated to us what they can be like
when they are invited to claim interesting words as their own.
The culture offered children the word

Supercalifragilisticexpialidocious

on the wings of a song.
We didn't tell the children they had to learn the word
before they were allowed to sing the song.
We didn't tell them that
if they were in the low reading group
we would give them a small, uninteresting word
to take the place of this complex, exciting word.
And the children responded to our freely given invitation.
It was so exciting going around the country
while "Mary Poppins" was in full swing.
The children demonstrated how they can behave
when their love of words is rewarded
by a truly worthwhile offering.
Not only could they read supercalifragilisticexpialidocious.
They could count the syllables and spell it backwards!

Words in the *Sounds of Language* reading program
are thought of as the personal possessions of each child.
At the end of reading a story or poem
you need only ask:

> *Did anyone hear a word*
> *you would like as your own?*

Once you give a child a word card
for each of his favorite words or phrases,
the fun begins!
Children will compare words.
They will swap with one another.
They will ask you for a blank card
to copy a friend's word.
They will arrange their word cards in patterns that

1) begin alike,
2) sound alike,
3) end alike.

They will create sentences on their desks.
Their favorite words are apt to appear
in their drawings and in their speech.

And you—think of the possibilities
for your involvement!
One bright, sunshiny morning you might announce:

> *Boys and girls,*
> *you'll never guess what I did last night.*
> *I sat up writing parts of sentences.*
> *When I hold one of these parts*
> *up in the air, if you have a word*
> *that will finish the sentence,*
> *hold it up.*

Suddenly your room will come alive
with thirty different sentences
as children hold up word cards to complete
a provocative sentence starter such as:

> *Someday I am going to kiss a _____.*

Cinderella

astronaut

skinny

afternoon

dinosaur

wago   dragon

magician

musician

piccolo player

scientific

horse face

Another day you might suggest:

Children, do you know what let's do today?
Let's put one rubber band
around the word cards you do recognize
and one around the words you don't.
Then supposing you choose
one unknown word each day
to work on and change over to your known words.

On other days the children can arrange their words alphabetically,
can group them with rubber bands
as naming words, action words, and describing words.
You can tell from this discussion,
that giving children word cards
is not the end,
but rather the beginning of a whole host
of language encounters
that help children claim the glory and workings of words.
Although it is true that filling out word cards
demands effort on your part,
you will find yourself basking in the rich rewards.
How exciting to have children ask for and value new words,
and through innate curiosity about things they value,
to analyze these words down to their most unique characteristic.
By the way, if you think alphabetizing
is the preferred way for arranging and filing word cards,
you may want to listen to your children.
Children have been known to make arrangements of

exciting words,
   letter writing words,
story writing words,
   hard words,
easy words,
   and even last week's words.

Interestingly enough, when children themselves
decide on methods of categorizing and filing,
they know exactly where to look for the word they need.

Those of you who teach older boys and girls
may be wondering how you can offer
the joy and productivity of word cards.
Actually, older boys and girls
have been known to do this same kind
of self-selected word collecting
with various kinds of word lists in their notebooks.
A boy who keeps a list of describing words worth using
when you want to indicate whether you're for or against a team,
is more highly motivated
than the boy who is idly writing sentences
using a list of *today's new words.*
Throughout the *Sounds of Language* program,
children are helped to analyze
the printed characteristics of words.
Surprisingly enough,
the most useful investigation
does not necessarily focus on beginnings and endings and middles.
In terms of a child's natural way for moving into print,
the first step in word analysis
is to hear and say the word orally
and count the number of syllables.
The sound of a word is its most unique characteristic
and it tends to be reflected in the printed symbol.
Let's pronounce and take a look at the word *station:*

The workmen
are going to build
a new police station here.

sta/tion

Ear and eye work comfortably together
in the word *station.*
It is easy to hear that there are two parts.
What are the useful steps to take in word analysis?

| First: | "*Let's listen to the word* station, *Chuck.* |
| | *How many sounds do you hear?*" |

Second: "*Look at the word, Chuck. (sta/tion)*
            I am writing it on the chalkboard the way you say it."

Third: "*Now read the sentence in which you found the word, Chuck.*
            Do you hear two sounds in station?"

Fourth: *You move from here to any next sensible step.*
             It might be to look
             at that intriguing tion *syllable*

             "*Let's look at some other two-syllable words*
             that look something like the word station.

sta	tion
na	tion
no	tion

Who knows where you go from here?
It might be to other two-syllable words
in the story, "The House Biter."
It might be to the wonderful
four-syllable word *education*
or to the intriguing *stationary*
that carries the original word *station*.

But whatever sequence you take,
you must be secure in the fact
that you can follow your own hunches
and your own common sense
in response to clues given by the children.
Children love to analyze a word they have discovered
in the context of a meaningful language pattern.
Let's not fool ourselves into believing
that there is only one sequence in word analysis.
Individual children and teachers have their own continuities
and this program invites you to respect these differences.

Then along came ALITTLEFISH

9 FIGURING OUT HOW PRINT WORKS

When a child looks at a page of print,
something dynamic must happen if we hope for him to become
an intelligent, self-motivated reader.
Oh, we can force him to read as we do in many programs,
but unless he himself elects to explore the page of print
in an effort to make sense out of it,
we can safely assume
that he is not learning much about reading.
The traditional answer to this
has been simply to write stories with scaled vocabulary
so that a child's eyes will immediately see familiar words,
but there is much more
that can encourage a child to explore a page of print
than the sighting of familiar words.

You will discover that on many pages of *Sounds of Language* readers,
the type swells, lurches, screams, whispers,
undulates, turns somersaults,
and even subsides in pictorial and narrative context.

It swam around, and around, and around, and around, and around, and around, and around, and around, and around, and around. It looked at the worm on the pin. It waggled its tail.

Our research shows that children find innovative type arrangements challenging.
They like to figure out where a line begins and where it is going and they
recognize the need to find the right beginning and direction if they are
to get the sound of sense in their reading. However, if you have a child who
might have a visual perception problem, it would be wise to exercise
professional judgment in using some of the unusual type portions of this book.

FOOD, GLORIOUS FOOD! HOT SAUSAGE & MUSTARD!

—from *Sounds of a Distant Drum*

Having type behave in intriguing ways is not foreign to children.
We adults have grown accustomed to schoolbooks
where the same size and style of type
move relentlessly from left to right, page after page,
and it is easy to forget that today's children are encountering
imaginative and flamboyant uses of type on TV,
in magazine advertising
and even on their cereal boxes.

Watch children's faces as they follow the dancing type
in *"Ten Little Indians"* from *Sounds I Remember.*
Notice how intently their eyes move with the type
and how their spirits buoy with the playful design.
In impressive ways these young children are learning
the most basic characteristic of type—
it moves from one place to another.

The sad fact is,
most of the early reading programs,
with their insistence on a rigid left-to-right
non-varying pattern of print,
actually cut children off from a fundamental cultural experience
which tells children that print is
a very versatile and exciting human invention
which to a large degree bends itself to the desires of the user.
Rules about beginning on the left and moving to the right
are not impressive invitations into the world of print.
It is a child's recognition that type moves,
a recognition that most easily comes
from pages where the movement is exaggerated,
and his determination to figure out the plan
back of the typographical puzzle
that motivate a child to make a go of reading.
Once he is caught up in the excitement
of following the movement of type as he reads,
he will himself come to the generalization
that for the most part in the English language,
type does move from left to right.

As you leaf through the *Sounds of Language* books,
you will discover that in addition to other
exciting typographical innovations,
the type generally is set in the pattern of spoken language,
just as the type in this essay
has been printed in facsimiles of oral language patterns.
Various methods have been used
to cause the reader to focus attention on selected words,

i   t relationships.
  m   n
    p   e
      o   r
        r   e
          t   h
            a   n
              n   n
                t ideas, and i

And now for a moment of frankness . . .
When you first looked at this series of books,
did you realize that it was for purposes
of helping children figure out how print works
that the books were designed as they are?
Children are curious about how print works,
just as they were curious about how spoken language works.
The *Sounds of Language* readers reward this curiosity
by helping children relate all that they know about spoken language
as they unravel the secrets of print
and make these secrets work for them.
You will want to help the children verbalize
their adventures with print in the *Sounds of Language* readers.

Children, can you see the shapes of those words
slurpy and glurpy? Take a close look.

—from *Sounds Around the Clock*

You may be a teacher who is worried that our innovative type arrangements will confuse children. Actually, our research shows the opposite to be true. Children like the intrigue of figuring out where a line begins and where it is going. They recognize that the sound of sense in what they are reading will help them find the right beginning and direction. They also recognize that the author leaves clues such as capital letters to send them on their way. It is the Sounds-of-Language focus on the sound of sense in reading that is significant. Being guided by the sound of sense is a much more fundamental reading act than following an arbitrary edict, "Always begin on the left." Moreover, if you are following the Sounds-of-Language method of reading stories and poems aloud to the children before they encounter them in print, the children will have an *auditory road map* to guide them on their visual trip through the sentence. If a child goes to a selection on his own without having heard it and he seems confused, just read the selection to him so his *auditory road map* can come into play. Several impressive experiences of this kind will invite children to use their ears as *road maps* even when they are reading on their own. If you discover a child with a serious visual problem, the type arrangements in this book merely help you identify the problem—they do not cause it; and it would be wise to seek professional help for the child.

and I, Trotting to market with cheeses and pie, Trotting to

Hey la la, Ho la, My donkey — and I. Hey la la, Ho la, Oh Donkey take care, If you should

Hey la la, Ho la, My donkey — never get there, Hey la la, Ho la, Oh Donkey take care. Hey la

'If you should stumble, we'll — My donkey and I, We'll eat — those cheeses, And we'll

buy, we'll eat those cheeses, — eat that pie, Hey la la, Ho la,

An old song, author unknown.
painting by Vic Herman

If no one should buy. — la, Ho la, If no one should

'If you should stumble, we'll never get there,

Hey la la, Ho la, My donkey — market with cheeses and pie,

—from *Sounds After Dark*

As the children pore over this especially designed page,
they are role-playing in exaggerated fashion
the fact that if a person studies the puzzle of a page of print
he will discover signals and patterns
that help him decode what he is encountering.

In a similar way
when a child looks at the printed page of the old song above
and says, "I know where that song begins,"
he is showing that he has found enough clues
to get a start on unravelling the puzzle.
Which clues worked for him?
Was it the capital letter? Starting on the left?
The space in the lower left-hand corner?
The actual clues he found do not matter as much as the fact
that he expects his search to be rewarded.

One indication that the children are beginning
to make typographical arrangements work for them
is their experimentation with intriguing arrangements
of words and letters and numbers in their own writing.
The more children can get the notion that written language
is an exciting and dependable puzzle
with multiple clues for the person who is reading,
the more confident and successful they will be
in their independent reading.

For the psychological advantages as well as for pure enjoyment,
from time to time write on the board
familiar sentences in reverse direction,
in scattered fields of letters,
in upright rocketing,
in straight downward plunges,
in crisscross fashion.
And even upside down and backwards.

Then watch the children delight
as they put all of their linguistic skills
into the decoding of the language.
It is dramatic experiences like these
that stand children in good stead
as they engage in the routine aspects of decoding.
Children will work at identifying initial consonants
or medial vowels or moving from left to right
with more personal determination and pleasure
when they see such activities
as part of the larger and more exciting process
of figuring out the puzzle of print.

10 DEVELOPING SKILL IN COMPREHENSION

Contrary to the view of many reading programs,
comprehension is not merely a matter
of the reader's proving that he has "read" the selection.

All too often this kind of proving simply means
listing main events, main characters, key words,
character traits, and snatches of figurative language.
Comprehension activities takes on true character
when they involve the reader or listener in such ways
that he comes to grips
with his and his colleagues' personal interpretations
in relation to the author's intended meanings.
If you care about this kind of comprehension,
much depends on the kind of questions you ask children.
For example, a question like

How far did John walk?

has only one possible answer to children
who have just read that John walked six miles.
Even if a child gives the "correct" answer,
what has he actually gained from this "educative process"?
As a matter of fact, the first child who gives the answer
closes the discussion.
The "educative process" comes to a close.
There is nowhere else the discussion could possibly go.
And how smart some children are in knowing
which children in the group will give the *correct answers* first!
Many simply do not expect to participate
in unimaginative rituals of this kind,
and gladly play the role of passive observers
because the situation structures such roles.

Think, on the other hand, what happens to children
if the teacher accepts the fact
that she doesn't have to make the children prove
that they have read the story threadbare,
and, therefore, can ask intriguing comprehension questions,
such as,

> *Children, the story says John walked six miles.*
> *How far is six miles?*

Every child now—even those who read less well than others—
views himself as an active participant in the discussion
and will gladly contribute his thoughts and feelings,
knowing that the purpose is to examine and probe personal meanings.

You may want to ask yourself if your questions
are the kind that stimulate thoughtful discussions
by which each reader can evaluate the meanings
he gleaned from and brought to the story.
Nothing is more exciting, more conducive to learning,
than to participate in a cross-fire of opinions and ideas
generated by a common experience, such as story meanings.
Here are some examples of questions
that will trigger off lively discussions
that will contribute to children's comprehension of the world
in which they live:

> *How long is a person young?*

The story "Growing Up, Growing Older" says,

> *John is now a young man.*
> *He is eighteen years old.*

How easy and unrewarding it would be to ask:

> *How old was John when he was a young man?*

A child could answer *18 years old* and be correct,
but what kind of thinking,
what kind of language usage,
what kind of mental and emotional involvements
does his answer promote?

The openness of a true comprehension question invites children
to put everything they know about life
(in this case, what constitutes being young or old)
into their answer.
It also invites all children to participate in the discussion,
not only he who happens to speak first.
And make no mistake!
When you ask children how long a person is young,
you are going to get an array of life-related answers.
Many a child feels old at six,
and anyone old enough to go to college is positively antiquated.

Your comprehension questions about a story
will trigger off a whole hierarchy of meanings
ranging from gross understanding to precise verbalizing,
from a simple restatement of story meanings
to a complex conjecture about the whole realm of living.

Annotated in *Sounds of Laughter* for the consideration of both you
and the children is the question:

> *Is it hard not to speak in anger*
> *when your heart is filled with anger?*

The children have just been reading
the story of an Indian boy and his grandfather
and they have heard the grandfather advise the boy
not to speak in anger.
But the concern of the moment is not the grandfather's advice.
The concern is the feelings of the alive children in your classroom
who are encountering this advice.
We must not assume that comprehension can be measured
only in terms of "correct" answers to tight little questions.
The important thing is,
each child is pitting his own meanings against the author's
and gradually coming to know what the story means to him.
The cross-pollenation that occurs
in such discussions
also invites children to question their own meanings
and even to organize new meanings.

Here are some examples of questions
that should trigger lively discussions
that will both focus the literary experience
and contribute to children's comprehension of human behavior.

A) *Did you ever stop to think that there could be
such a thing as a bird that doesn't fly?
What makes a bird a bird anyway?*
"At Home on the Ice," *Sounds of a Hound Dog*

B) *If Bill held an after-school job for which he was paid a salary,
would he, after finding the trapped duck, have
ignored the reporting-in time, just as he did
when it was time to report in to his mother at dark?
Would you?* "The Web of Winter," *Sounds of Mystery*

C) *Do you like Mr. Lincoln better with or without a beard?
Why?* "A Vote for a Beard," *Sounds of a Young Hunter*

D) *Well, children, what do you think
of a free-wheeling literary-artistic-dramatic-boisterous
story like this?*
"How Old Stormalong Captured Mocha Dick," *Sounds of a Distant Drum*

Another insightful way of getting into
a full-blown discussion of story meanings
is to ask questions that relate to the author or artist's techniques
of putting a story or a picture together.

A) *A comparison of the descriptive line in "Facts About
Angry Bears"
with the dramatic story line in "Little Balser and the
Big Bear"
(or any other comparison of a factual article
with a story with a strong plot), for example,
will reveal much of children's understanding of the
selections,
although, ostensibly, they are discussing literary
structure.* —from *Sounds of a Young Hunter*

B) *What has the artist done in this picture to convey*
   to you that this is a make-believe story?
   "The Battle of the Furniture," *Sounds Jubilee*

C) *What clues do you get from the title and the illustrations*
   as to what kind of reading you will find in this selection?
   "The Birth and Growth of a Tree," *Sounds of a Distant Drum*

Enough comprehension questions have been annotated
throughout this program
to give you the feel of framing open-ended questions
that promote a depth of comprehension and feelings of self-respect.
Once you have experienced
the dynamics of a vital group discussion,
in contrast to a boring kind of question-answer ritual,
you will be well on your way to becoming that kind of teacher
whom children remember and revere.
The art of good teaching has deep roots
in the ability to motivate meaningful discussions.
Of course, post reading discussions are not the only way
for children to organize their reading meanings.
When the fourth grade teacher reads

Giant Thunder striding home

wonders if his supper's done.

'Hag wife, Hag wife, bring me my bones!'

   'They are not done,' the old hag moans.

'Not done? not done?' the giant roars

and heaves his old wife out of doors.

and Bill blurts out "*Sounds just like my father!*"
it is not necessary to ask a lot of tight little questions
about who came striding home and what wasn't done.
Bill's comprehension is proved in his spontaneous response
and the laughter of his classmates
is ample proof that Bill's comprehension is shared.

When the kindergarten teacher opens to the title page
of an honest-to-goodness spooky book
and Therese promptly gets up from her place
at the teacher's feet
and moves as far away from the book as possible
while still remaining in hearing range,
there is little doubt but that Therese understands
the mood of the story.
And as the story progresses
and Therese keeps moving back and forth—
now near the book, now far away—
she is using her entire body
to express her comprehension of the story.
Six-year-old Brenda's spontaneous response to A. A. Milne's line

So I think I'll be six now for ever and ever.

—from *Sounds Around the Clock*

needs no explanation.

I do not want to be six for ever because I want to be a nurse because I want to help people and a whole gob of people will say thank you. Brenda

—1st Grade, J. J. Ingalls School, Kansas City, Kansas

Children are bubbling with spontaneous responses
to stories and poems until they learn
that there is only one thing that happens
after reading a story:
the teacher asks questions.
If your children do not seem to respond spontaneously
and you have a notion it is because
they are in this other habit of thinking about story response,
you may have to be the one in your class who responds
spontaneously to a story
in order to get the whole spontaneous,
personalized reaction-thing going.
After reading about John and his six mile walk,
for example, if you slap yourself on the thigh
and exclaim

> *WOW! What an idiot!*

and in other ways role-play the fact
that this kind of responding is a legitimate way
for showing comprehension,
the children will soon pick up the invitation
and reading time will take on more life.

And of course you are aware
that painting and dancing and creative dramatics
are also productive ways
for organizing personal meanings
brought into play by a story or poem or article.

One last thought about comprehension.
You may be interested to reread our discussion
FIGURING OUT HOW STORIES AND POEMS WORK, page 24.
And **FIGURING OUT HOW SENTENCES WORK**, page 56.
In both of these teaching strategies
are numerous suggestions
of times when the structure of a story or poem or sentence
deeply influences the meaning.
Those of us who study language in human affairs
can only conclude that structure is itself
one expression of meaning.

The post-reading discussions in *Sounds of Language*
that are triggered off by the open-ended comprehension questions
and by certain language-analysis questions

    A) put each child in touch with his own thoughts and
           feelings that have been generated by the reading,

    B) put him in touch with the feelings and thoughts
           of other children who supposedly shared an "identical"
           reading experience, and

    C) help him verbalize his growing insights
           into the workings of language, both in oral and written
           form.

The child's self-expressions, therefore, have a rare dynamic quality
as he searches for verbal ways to express the inner growth
that his reading occasioned.
Every speaking skill he employs,
everything from sentence patterns to figures of speech,
is influenced by the integrity of his speaking situation.
His *preciseness* in self-expression, therefore,
actually is preciseness in making language work to express
and thereby validate his own personality.

11 LINKING WRITING TO READING

In *Sounds of Language* children are helped
to develop writing skills
in the same naturalistic, linguistically sound ways
that they learn to read.
Just as kindergarteners and young first graders
latch on to highly structured rhymes and stories
and role-play themselves as readers,
these same young children begin innovating
on the author's pattern and role-play themselves as writers.

Hello! My name is Pamela, K.
I am a maker of costumes.
I make funny costumes and scary
costumes. These are the
costumes I make.

—2nd Grade, J. J. Ingalls School
Kansas City, Kansas

Gradually they learn to use their *Sounds of Language* books
as resource books for personal writing.
They know that these books are crammed
with story patterns and rhyme schemes and sentence patterns
that are theirs for the asking.
They also know that they have the practical know-how,
transforming sentences, for example,
for taking an author's structure
and hanging their own thoughts on it.

As one young child exultantly declared
after borrowing the literary structure
and sentence patterns of "The Billy Goats Gruff"
to successfully write his own story about three skunks
who encountered a troll on their way to eat garbage:

I only needed three new words
for my whole story—
> skunk
> *and* garbage
> *and* smelly.

I almost needed the word stinked
so I could say
the skunk stinked the troll,
but I remembered
you gave me the word skunk
and I could use that to say
the skunk skunked *him.*

—from Mueller School, second grade, Wichita, Kansas

Once children become accustomed to using their reader this way,
you will be amazed by both the quality and quantity
of their writing.
Moreover, you will have a solution to the nagging problem
of what kinds of "seat work" to provide the rest of the class
while you are busy with a few children.

12 CULTIVATING LITERARY AND ESTHETIC APPRECIATION

The content of the *Sounds of Language* readers
is specifically planned to place literary appreciation
at the heart of the reading program.
From the very first day of first grade
throughout the entire elementary school experience,
children using *Sounds of Language* readers
will be living in the midst of a gallery of contemporary art
and in a climate of literary appreciation
that sensitize their responses and imprint their memories
with high idealism and soul-stirring emotions.

Esthetic response can only be nurtured.
It cannot be taught.
By a wide and continuing exposure
to stories, poems, art, photos, and language
that possess some pretension to taste,
children will begin to know what they do and do not like.
Knowing what one does not like
is equally important as knowing what one enjoys.
Whatever else, a child's response must be self-selected,
and it must be sincere.
We teachers need to learn how to live with children's responses
which move against the grain of our own preferences
and which reveal pleasure in the mundane.
Many children, for example, will necessarily go
through a long period of literary exposure
before they are apt to sense the worthwhileness
of Emily Dickinson's poem "Autumn"
as compared to the joy they found in their favorite comics.

Be assured that those pleasurable times of the day
when you read aloud to children
are all a part of a program in literary and esthetic appreciation,
as well as a part of the reading program.

One especially productive technique
for helping children make these kinds of value judgments
comes about through an adaptation of Sidney Simon's value line
suggested in the drawing on the opposite page.
Simply list a few of the stories and/or poems and/or articles
the children have been reading
and suggest that they rate each one
by placing it in a self-selected spot
on their own copy of the value line.
In order to help the children understand
that the value line is not an instrument
for placing one selection at the low end of the line,
another at the high end,
and the rest at equal intervals along the line,
you might want to engage them in conversation
about their use of the line.
Help them understand that the value line
does not only apply to the seven stories
they are rating at this time.
The value line has places for all the stories
they have or ever will read.
The seven stories they are rating today
might all fall at the middle or top of the line.
Or they might scatter up and down the line.
You see, the value line is actually part of each of us.
It is man's way
for placing a value on things he encounters in life.
The value line might be used to rate happenings
or foods or school subjects or teachers or movies, etc.
The important thing to remember is—
there is no special ruler to measure the experiences of such stories, etc.
and to place them on the value line.
It is a person's response from his value
that places them one place or another on the value line.

Don't try to tell the children all about the line
at one sitting.
Put the line on the board
and start using it informally,

asking the children for suggestions
as to where some of the stories might fall.
As you talk together and the children differ
about certain ratings,
they will come to understand how the line works.
After a few minutes, suggest that they draw their own lines
and place the seven stories where they want them.

1) *House Afire!*

2) *When Christmas Comes*

3) *The Grandmother*

4) *The Ax*

5) *The Mice Who Loved Words*

6) *The First Schlmiel*

7) *Every Man Heart Lay Down*

—selections from *Sounds Jubilee*

LOW   MID   HIGH

Once the children have placed the stories somewhere on the line,
the fun begins.
Invite the children to meet as a group
to discuss their various placements.
How your classroom will ring with developing values
as the children explain and even defend
their various designations on the line!
And what a basic learning for the children
when they discover that three people can read the very same story
and come up with highly different evaluations—
all of which can be defended.
They might even deduce that if three different teachers
rather than just one gave them report card grades,
they would come up with differing marks.

13 DEVELOPING SENSITIVITY TO THE THREE LEVELS OF LANGUAGE

Sounds of Language rejects the notion of "right" and "wrong"
in judging a child's language performance.
We recognize, instead, that there are three levels of language
that every child has a right
to experiment with, enjoy, and claim as his own.

A) Home-Rooted Language

The first level of language,
indigenous to the child's life itself,
is his *home-rooted (in-group) language.*
This language may or may not be grammatically correct.
It is the language he inherited from his family,
the language that is native to his soul
and sounds best to his ear.
This language may or may not feed comfortably
into the classroom,
but if we want our classrooms to be language laboratories
where a child feels free to experiment
with new linguistic patterns,
we must first of all respect the language he brings to school.
Both you and the children may be surprised to see
the number of selections in *Sounds of Language*
that are written in *home-rooted language.*
This can help both you and the children
better respect vernacular for its beauty
and for its direct communicative impact.
Isn't it fortunate that folklore
has helped us keep the richness of home-rooted language
in the bloodstream of our language heritage!

A copperhead snake made for me
one day when I was hoein' my corn.
Happened I saw him in time,
and I lit into him with the hoe.

He thrashed around,
bit the hoe-handle a couple of times,
but I fin'lly killed him.
Hung him on the fence.
Went on back to work,

—from "The Snakebit Hoe-handle," *Sounds of a Young Hunter*

For a picture of what linguistic heights
young children can reach
when their home-rooted language is respected,
see the dictated story from a young primary child
on the next page.
Obviously someone had read "The Billy Goats Gruff"
to this child, and just as obviously,
the child stored the basic structure of the story
in his linguistic storehouse.
Notice how faithful he is to the fact
that this is a story organized around a problem.
How faithful he is to the repetition in the episodes!
How faithful he is to the solving of the problem!
If the school had *made* him feel uncomfortable about his language,
he would have "dried up" and looked like one of those "children
without language"
we hear so much about.
We ourselves wonder if it is so much a matter
of "children without language"
as it is a matter of children who have been asked in effect
to check their home-rooted language outside the classroom door.

Them all going up to the grass where you eat and the mean old troll said "Who walkin' on my bridge?" I comin' up to eat you and little Billy Goat said "Don't eat me. Wait for my next brother to come.

So da troll said O.K. I will wait. So he waited and the next brother comed and the big old troll said who walkin on my bridge. Me, next billy goat Gruff. Wait don't eat me wait.

Then boomp boomp I comin up to eat you. So he did. He tossed the mean old troll up to the sky and eat him all up.

B) Public Language

The second level of language is *public language*.
This is the corps of language ways
that society uses to carry on its organized life.
It is the grammatically correct language that facilitates
broad and precise communication with the English-speaking community.
When standards of "right" and "wrong" are used
to evaluate language (heaven forbid!)
public language is the form that is said to be "right."
Public language should not be made available to children,
on the basis of "right" and "wrong,"
but rather as one of three ways to express themselves.

Different situations call for different kinds of language.
Just as public language works best in some situations,
so does home-rooted language in others.
When a child knows that he has a choice in language usage,
public language for him gains intrigue and respect.
Many articles and essays in *Sounds of Language* are written
in public language
to help children appreciate its direct, uncluttered, and practical
effectiveness.

> Most of the Indian tribes
> of the early American frontier
> lived by hunting buffalo
> and other animals.
> These tribes were wanderers.
> They were good hunters
> and fierce warriors.
>
> —from *Sounds of a Distant Drum*

Westfield, Chautauque Co NY
Oct 15, 1860
Hon A B Lincoln
Dear Sir
My father has just come from the fair and brought home your picture and mr Hamlin's.

—from *Sounds of a Young Hunter*

The children may be interested in discussing
why Grace Bedell chose public language
when writing her letter to Abraham Lincoln.
This can lead to a discussion
of whether certain home-rooted expressions
might be appropriate in a letter to a best friend, to a stranger.
These discussions of language choices
give children feelings of power and pleasure
about themselves as language users.

Developing Sensitivity to the Three Levels of Language TE 123

C) Life-Lifting Language

Sing hey! Sing hey!
For Christmas Day
Twine mistletoe and holly
For friendship glows
In winter snows,
And so let's all be jolly.

— an old rhyme from *Sounds of a Young Hunter*

The third level of language is *life-lifting (literary) language.*
It is any bit or unit of language,
such as a story or poem or expression,
that is so memorable that it tends
to impress itself indelibly on the mind
and thereby become part of the culture's cherished language ways.

In
December   *"Get*
autumn   *ready*
calls   *for a*
its   *winter*
warning,   *morning!"*

It has been our experience
that many children whose home-rooted language
does not open-end comfortably into the public language
take on the public forms more easily
through poetry and other literature
than they do in lessons on public language.

Peck

     peck

       peck

on the warm brown egg.

OUT comes a neck.

OUT comes a leg.

    How

       does

          a chick,

     who's not been about,

     discover the trick

     of how to get out?

—"Baby Chick" by Aileen Fisher,
Sounds of Numbers

Consider the language thrust that any child will receive
if, throughout his elementary school years,
he has such broad and continuous exposure to memorable language
that he intakes into his mind's treasury
twenty or more poems a year.
This experience in and of itself
provides a major bridge for any child
into the culture's language storehouse,
and, at the same time, fills his mind
with high idealism and humanistic feelings.
The pervasive use of choral reading and choral speaking
in *Sounds of Language* is geared to this end.

Speak gently, Spring, and make no sudden sound;

For in my windy valley, yesterday I found

New-born foxes squirming on the ground—

    Speak gently.

—from "Four Little Foxes" by Lew Sarett,
Sounds of a Storyteller

Developing Sensitivity to the Three Levels of Language TE 125

> All: We sing of thee, America,
> Land we love, America,
> Hear our song of Liberty,
> Our country 'tis of thee.
> Narrator: Our country 'tis of thee we sing,
> land of New England meadows and southern cottonfields,
> of county fairs, and ticker-tape parades,
> barefoot boys with fishing rods
> and Ladies' Day at the baseball park.
> A land of steel,
> and industry,
> and invention
> with a heart as big as Texas
> and dreams as tall as the great Northwest.
> All: But where did it all begin?
> Who made it possible?
> Narrator: Well, to start with
> There was a man ...

—from "Our Country 'Tis of Thee,"
Sounds of a Distant Drum

Moreover, the choral speaking and choral reading
that children continuously do as part of this reading program
help them develop an appetite for the life-lifting language of literature.
As children's ears begin to know the pleasures
of this kind of language and this kind of reading,
their whole disposition toward life as well as toward literature
is affected.

In developing attitudes of literary discrimination,
each child should be encouraged to keep a running list
of his five favorite stories and poems.
Whenever he wants to add a new favorite to his list,
he necessarily must decide which of his former favorites
must be removed.
Only by exercising his own judgment in these matters,
without interference by an over-anxious adult,
will he gradually refine his sensitivities to literary ways.